'Gripping – but more ... speculative writing. Ste... ...lled as the natural successor to Clarke, Asimov and Heinlein for the hard science in his novels . . . Read, be awed and amazed at our deep future, but be prepared to lose sleep.'   *SFX*

'It's smart, thought-provoking stuff, surfing the outer edges of physics and making a plea for colonisation of the planets . . . One of his more interesting notions is that there might not be other intelligent life in the universe. Somehow he manages to make this bleak, somewhat depressing thought seem like a wonderful opportunity for our species.'

Stan Nicholls, *Time Out*

'Baxter's academic background in physics affords telling insights into what might be possible in the future, while the gift for lush narrative and enthusiasm for the natural world that inspired the *Mammoth* trilogy makes this an exhilarating read . . . a surprisingly beautiful and haunting vision.'

Mike Woods, Waterstones Online.

'Like his mentor Arthur C. Clarke, Baxter coins evocative phrases . . . *Deep Future* is a lively though often chilling tour of possible futures, looking afresh at classic speculations (from Freeman Dyson, Carl Sagan and many others) and updating them for our new millennium.'

David Langford, Amazon.co.uk

'Baxter's creative writing has long been held in esteem by readers of science fiction . . . Baxter's ability to use present day metaphors to illustrate his projections lend an extra dimension to his work, forcing the reader to consider aspects of the future they may previously have taken for granted.'

Dreamwatch

●

STEPHEN BAXTER
DEEP FUTURE

The right of Stephen Baxter to be identified as the author
of this work has been asserted by him in accordance
with the Copyright, Designs and Patents Act 1988.

Published in Great Britain in 2002 by
Victor Gollancz
An imprint of Orion Books Ltd
Orion House, 5 Upper St Martin's Lane,
London WC2H 9EA

A CIP catalogue record for this book
is available from the British Library

ISBN 0 575 072865

Printed in Great Britain by
Clays Ltd, St Ives plc

Contents

Part Four: Pilots of the Purple Twilight

Part Five: Deep Future

Acknowledgements

Sections of this book appeared in substantially different versions in the magazines *Alien Encounters, Astronomy Now, Focus, Foundation, Frontiers, Journal of the British Interplanetary Society, Matrix, New Scientist, Spaceflight,* and *T3*.

of any sort without continued physical survival, in one form or another.

And the logic, as we will see, is irrefutable. If we continue to survive, our future *must* be something like that depicted in this book.

The future is hurtling toward us, whether we like it or not. But we don't have to be afraid. In our time, the future is no longer Shakespeare's undiscovered country; it is becoming a place we can map and explore.

ONE

•

A Dangerous Century

Chapter 1

The Onrushing Future

I never think of the future. It comes soon enough.
— Albert Einstein

Einstein was right: the future rushes toward us relentlessly, a minute every minute, without cease or pity. But let's think of it even so.

To see the future is an ancient dream. As a child in the 1960s, drinking in the wonderful TV shows of Gerry Anderson, I grew up believing that the future of 2065 would be a place of silvery suits and jet cars and colonies in space. But when I asked my father what it would *really* be like, he replied, with bluff good sense, 'Man had to wear suits a hundred years ago, and I bet they will still be wearing suits a hundred years from now.'

Of course, much does change, even over a short time span. For proof, try rerunning a home video of five or ten years ago. Look at the minutiae – the ads, the hairstyles, the clothes: much of it will seem foreign indeed, even so close in time. And yet much else stays the same.

What then, if you could step out of your door, right now, and walk into the future – let's say, the year 2100?

*

At first glance you might believe that nothing has changed at all.

After all, the basic elements of a city – roads, buildings – haven't changed much in the *past* century. But look a little closer.

Modern advances in materials, science and building design will transform our cities. Imagine a building so smart that it could ride out an earthquake like a commuter riding out the bumps on a rush-hour train. Imagine a road, bridge or a pavement made of a self-healing concrete – no more road works! Imagine a sharp corner that cried out if it spotted you coming too close, or if it sensed some internal failure approaching. This is the sensual city: drenched by information technology, almost alive, responsive to its own needs, and yours.

The future doesn't necessarily mean changing everything. The future can be subtle. It must, after all, grow out of the present. Things may look the same – but under the surface, everything is different. But this may seem a claustrophobic place to modern eyes, over-protective, like a huge nursery.

The roads don't seem to have changed much. The traffic is bumper to bumper, all day and all night. Maybe the cars look a little sleeker. But they seem to be going awfully fast, and awfully close together. And now you spot a driver actually asleep behind the wheel, with his hands behind his head, dozing away as his car races along at a hundred and fifty kilometres per hour – no more than a metre from the car in front!

Well, don't worry, because the cars have got smarter too. They have sensors to monitor the road and the position of all the surrounding vehicles. Computers control the acceleration, the braking and the steering. The cars can talk to satellites to plot routes to avoid traffic jams. Maybe the cars even talk to each other over radio links, so that cars at the back of a queue react smoothly to changes at the front. Thanks to this virtual safety belt, there have been no deaths from road accidents for fifty years.

All this is following a very clear trend of the present day: computers, information technology, are going to get smarter, but also smaller, and more pervasive. Science fiction writers of the past tended to imagine big mainframes – monolithic metal minds that filled rooms and had a persistent tendency to try to become God. Well, that was one prediction that went wrong. The computers of the future are more like an infection: intelligence is everywhere, miniaturised, in our cars, in our communication devices, in our clothes, even in ourselves.

You're feeling a little future shock, and so you stop in a restaurant to take a break. You nibble complimentary peanuts while you choose – at least you think they're peanuts . . . What's on the menu? Here's a Brazilian feijoada: pig's feet, tails and ears, with black beans, and all washed down with white rum. Hmm. Maybe. What's that lady having for a starter over there? It looks like pitta bread and humus. But it's actually an African delicacy this time: termites, mashed up with olive oil. And this bowl you've been nibbling at doesn't contain peanuts at all – again from Africa, it's dried mpane worms! Twenty-one hundred is a more cosmopolitan age, and the menu has dishes from parts of the world that are still relatively unknown to us Westerners.

All this is a consequence of globalisation, one of the *megatrends* which are shaping our future. But the future will always contain small stories as well as large: it's perhaps a sobering thought that by 2100 somebody has got seriously rich by being the first entrepreneur to import Zambian baobab fruit to London or Hamburg.

You turn to the newspaper (which, of course, is a me-paper, with all the news specially selected for your preference, downloaded from a satellite, and presented on a computer screen which you can fold up like a sheet of paper – or perhaps it is even tattooed to your wrist). The main headline is about an alien life form. A legal battle has been waged by well-wishers in the World Supreme Court to have these aliens recognised as sentient, and with rights equal to those of humans. After a century of persecution, we're no longer allowed to hunt down and kill these strangers in our midst.

But these alien creatures didn't arrive from another star: we *made* them. They are able to propagate, and evolve, and breed – all the characteristics of life – and they live within the huge, world-pervading computer systems. And, in 2100, they have the right to uninterrupted existence.

I'm talking, of course, about computer viruses – or rather the intelligent, much more complex descendants of the viruses of today. Except that in 2100 the world 'virus' is an insult, a mark of prejudice, which I wouldn't repeat in polite society.

Stephen Hawking has said that it's entirely typical of humanity that when we do get around to creating a life form – the virus – it's useless, malevolent, and we immediately try to crush it out of existence. But maybe this will change: perhaps the first step in the rehabilitation of the viruses is already at hand. Online shopping companies use software agents that roam the Internet and return information to the customer on, for example, the current best choice in clothes, records or books. Perhaps we will think of these benevolent cousins of the viruses as computer 'bacteria', tailored to be positively helpful, not harmful.

In 2100, despite the legal case, we continue to debate whether these software creatures really are conscious or not. The jury is still out; these entities are simply too different from us fragile biochemical creatures for meaningful comparisons of consciousness to be possible. But we have learned a harsh lesson from the way we treated our sentient biological cousins: we drove the chimp and the dolphin and the whale and the elephant to extinction long before we understood that they were just as conscious as we are, in their unique and different ways. And, certainly, we long not to be alone in the universe. So we give the viruses the benefit of the doubt.

The example of the computer virus illustrates a perhaps gloomy point: that some aspects of the future will remain almost impossible to predict. Even without technical changes, there are *emergent phenomena* (like the viruses) which arise from the sheer complexity of our systems, with the potential to cause us technical, ethical, social and other problems. But it's hard to anticipate such phenomena before the complexity is in place: you can't have traffic jams without the traffic. All we can do in the face of such unpredictability is prepare as best we can, and react to the future with flexible minds.

And certainly the arrival on Earth of a new intelligence, with independence of decision-making and action, is an epochal event.

Some aspects of the future are more predictable. The great mega-trends embedded in the present and identified by the futurologists are clear signposts to the world to come. And certainly one trend we can ride to the future of 2100 is demographic.

Walking around your future town or city you are struck by the large number of old people, the small number of the young. It is a silver society.

Advances in the understanding of the ageing process and the conquest of disease – for example, cancer should soon become a manageable condition, like diabetes – will dramatically extend the average life span. (Much of this is a consequence of our increasingly detailed mastery of the human genome, the genetic software that controls much of our destinies. In 2100 there will be (extravagantly paid) genome programmers – and, much more sinister, genome hackers . . .)

But, at the same time as the number of old people increases, the number of young is falling; birth rates are dropping in most advanced nations. The world is growing older.

There is no technical quick fix for such a problem. It will require delicate social adjustment with compromise on all sides. A nightmare scenario is a world of enclaves of old people, jealously guarding their wealth and power, living off the labour of the disenfranchised young. Perhaps there are even darker prospects: we greying folk must hope that euthanasia never becomes an instrument of social adjustment.

Of course there is a silver lining to every cloud. In 2100, you learn, the birth rate is actually so low that a form of conscription has been introduced: it has become compulsory for all young people to have unprotected sex with each other at least three times a week . . .

What about the bigger picture? If you dig a little deeper into your me-paper you find that the nation you left behind no longer exists. If you live in Europe, your grandchildren are citizens of a new United States: we Europeans all love each other now, and everything is marvellous – although it has taken the mother of all rows to get us to that point.

In the near future, the European Union will surely continue to expand and to be a force for peace (for example by subsuming the Balkans). Military technology world-wide may evolve in the direction of police actions: we will see more non-lethal weapons to disable rather than kill combatants. But to succeed in even the most limited ambitions the EU must absorb ancient nations with very different traditions; and much work is needed to improve European accountability and democracy.

Happily, by the year 2100, we have long sorted it all out. There was a constitutional convention in 2020: an ambition already argued for by political parties in Britain and Germany – and, after all, the Americans managed as much centuries ago. And the grand debate was not restricted to the politicians, the great and the good, but genuinely participatory, involving a high proportion of Europe's online electorate. It was indeed one heck of a row – and not every nation stayed to join the party – but in the end we made it through, and there was a grand signing ceremony of the Constitution in United Europe's new capital: London . . .

But the future is about more than demographics and politics. Perhaps we grown-ups are sometimes too grim, too sober in our imaginings.

Tired, a little overwhelmed, you are about to return home. On impulse, you look up for one last glimpse – and you see a sky crowded with even more cars, following invisible lanes in suspiciously clean air, their solar cell panels gleaming like the wings of bugs. Today, various companies are working on prototypes of air cars. And software engineering is advancing to the point where the major challenge to three-dimensional transport systems – traffic control – is becoming soluble. Jet cars! – just as advertised in the comics.

And, far above the flying cars, there are advertisements painted by lasers on the clouds: seductive images of holidays in Earth orbit, and at the Apollo 11 theme park on the Moon. At the time of writing, many organisations propose space tourism within ten years.

This may sound like my fondly remembered 1965 vision of the future – jet cars, holidays in space – but maybe, in some degree, the future really will turn out to be the way we expected when we were children.

But how is it possible to say, with any degree of certainty, what even the nearest of futures may hold for us?

Chapter 2

Past and Future

Study the past, if you would divine the future.
— Confucius

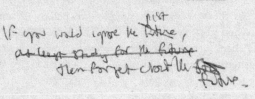

However fantastic its predictions, the future divination we are attempting in this book is not in any way mystical. This is not astrology; we are not picking lottery numbers from out of the stars. We are striving to be more scientific: to predict how the future might genuinely turn out.

I can assert without fear of contradiction that it *is* possible to tell the future successfully, at least to some extent. How do I know? Because there are people who make money out of it.

Think of all the professional forecasters in the modern world. Insurance companies have to gamble their profits on the future pattern of claims by their policy-holders. Stockbrokers, industry analysts, economists and politicians make or lose fortunes foreseeing the trends in economies and markets: there are even types of stock called 'futures', which essentially entail betting on future values. Intelligence and defence analysts expend much effort in 'war gaming' and other activities, trying to anticipate the actions of individuals and nations. There are whole legions of futurologists and forward planners employed by industry, government and academia. Even science itself is a form of future-telling. A scientist must build on experimental results to make predictions about the outcome of future experiments, predictions that can be validated or falsified.

Think of bookmakers!

Much of this relentless prophesying is benign; countless lives are saved by predictions of weather, geological calamity, and so on. No forecasters get it right a hundred per cent of the time, of course. And some systems seem to be unpredictable *in principle*. Chaos theory describes the way complex systems can behave in unpredictable ways when small perturbations can have large effects. The application of chaos theory to weather forecasting is well known: if the beat of a butterfly's wings in China can cause a hurricane in Florida, how can I tell whether to pack a brolly next Tuesday? (It is worth remembering that you can forecast the weather with seventy-seven per cent accuracy simply by assuming that tomorrow's weather will be more or less the same as today; Britain's Meteorological Office, for all its investment and technology, achieves only ten per cent better.)

Still, these legions of guess-makers get it right often enough to make it worth employing them. So how *can* you tell the future? And what are the limits of forecasting?

There are three main groups of forecasting methods.

First, if a process is simple enough – if it's dominated by one or two physical laws – then it's readily predictable. For instance, the orbits of the planets and other bodies around the sun – dominated by a single law, that of gravity – are known with great precision; we can predict solar eclipses and planetary conjunctions centuries ahead.

(Incidentally, regarding astronomical predictions it may be that by the year 2100, the most important date in history will be 7 August 2046, the most important name 1999 AN10. 1999 AN10 is an asteroid which is going to make several close approaches to Earth, and 7 August 2046 is the most likely date for an actual collision. The orbits are complex and difficult to determine; at the time of writing the odds of a collision are given by NASA as one in half a million. But

•

15

the odds quoted six months earlier were longer, at one in ten million. If those odds keep falling, all bets are off . . .)

Second, for more complex events, you can use statistical methods. The insurance companies' actuarial tables are an example. They can't predict precisely when exactly any of us will die, but they can predict with reasonable accuracy the percentage of the population to have died by a certain age.

Third, you can follow trends, the great engines of history which drive us into the future: population growth, climate adjustment, changes to the supply of food and water, etc. You pick some trend which you see in the world around you – such as global warming – and follow it to its extreme. *If this goes on*, what's the result? The predictions are familiar, if gloomy, in the case of global warming: melting polar ice caps, rising sea levels, wheat fields becoming dust bowls . . .

Trend-watching does have it drawbacks, of course, because things often don't carry on in a convenient straight line. To quote the economist Sir Alexander Cairncross:

> A trend is a trend is a trend
> But the question is: will it bend?
> Will it alter its course through some unforeseen force
> And come to a premature end?

Many serious people in London in the 1870s thought that if the then current trend in horse-drawn traffic continued, within a few decades the traffic would be moving at walking pace and we would all be knee deep in manure. As it turned out, of course, there was a *discontinuity*: the rise of the motor car, which changed all the trends in transportation. Now, we are indeed moving at walking pace, but we're knee deep in carbon monoxide instead.

Not all forecasting methods are rigorous – but then, not all fields are amenable to hard fact and decisive tests. It is much harder to spot trends in society and industry than to forecast, say, the outcome of an experiment in the physical sciences. In the 1960s and 1970s there was much interest in 'Delphi polling', in which experts in a field were consulted on a topic of future interest and an 'average' of their projections taken, the idea being to find an 'unbiased' view. The method was flawed by its frequent degeneration into a poll of fashionable views, and many Delphi panels tended to be stuffed with the 'usual suspects' in any given field, leading to predictable (and predictably wrong) results. But in some quarters the method is currently being re-evaluated, with safeguards against such problems.

It is remarkable that all our future-divining methods, in one way or another, are based on studying the past, just as Confucius counselled. But our efforts to map the future are not helped by the fact that – even without chaotic effects, even if the future were robust and stable – our knowledge of the past is less than perfect.

The historical record is woefully incomplete, and distorted besides. It is a truism that history is written by the victors. History is a tool used by propagandists, nation-builders, evangelists and others. Sometimes the distortions have a more innocent origin: each historian must interpret and extrapolate from the limited material available, and, embedded in her own culture, inevitably acts as a distorting lens through which we must view her subject.

And we are a story-telling species, forever seeking to make perfect narratives from the muddy complexity of the universe we find ourselves in. Psychological experiments have shown that we humans are prone to 'confabulation'. We edit our memories to construct 'stories' which make sense out of a chaotic world, and which give ourselves prominent and pleasing roles. We seek story, not necessarily truth.

Even the best-known figures of the past were surely very different in person from the portraits delivered to us by history. And the greatest shock of all is that some of our heroes never even existed.

Consider Robin Hood, for example. Under the pitiless glare of modern scholarship Robin has melted away into legend and confabulation, leaving not a trace of historical truth. His legend stemmed, in fact, from a series of fourteenth-century English ballads born out of a time of baronial rebellions and agrarian discontent, which culminated in the Peasants' Revolt of 1381. The notion of a free but persecuted outlaw, enjoying the forest's forbidden hunting while outwitting the forces of law and order, resonated at a time of deep popular resentment of authority. The familiar embroidery – Maid Marian and Friar Tuck, Robin's relocation to Nottinghamshire from Yorkshire, the idea that Robin was a fallen nobleman – mostly came about in the post-mediaeval period.

Even more modern nations than Robin's England are haunted by their confabulated heroes and heroines. Betsy Ross, for example, did exist. She was born Elizabeth Griscom. She took over her husband's upholstery business after he had been killed during the War of Independence. Later, she branched out into the manufacture of flags for the Pennsylvania Navy. But she was never visited by George Washington; she was not asked to make a flag for the new nation; she did not work on its design with Washington; she did not make up the flag in her back parlour. As far as can be determined, all of this was a concoction of her grandson's, almost a century later. But it was a nice story.

Davy Crockett's myth was self-manufactured. Though he was raised with little schooling in the backwoods of Tennessee, Crockett hunted very few racoons or bears, and fought fewer Indians. He filled his campaign speeches with homespun metaphors and yarns, but when elected to Congress, he developed several business ventures and used conventional English: there is no record of him ever having used the phrase 'b'ar-hunting' on the Hill. His coonskin legend was developed fairly cynically during his own lifetime to create popularity by the Whig party in Congress, and after he died it was further elaborated into a folk epic. But still, Crockett's death at the Alamo, that small, resonant pinprick of bravery, was noble.

The unravelling of such myths, and understanding the reasons why a figure like Robin Hood has held such fascination for so long, may prove more interesting than the myths themselves. But still, we must regret the loss of fond, harmless and even inspirational illusions.

And sometimes the absence of any historical core at all is deeply shocking. The case of Moses is notorious. Moses's career appears to be a conflation of the biographies of several leaders of the Biblical era, as the nation of Israel emerged from Palestinian refugees fleeing the collapse of Canaanite city-states. The rest seems to be invention or borrowing. The tale of him being concealed in a wicker basket and floated down the Nile, in order to save him from murder as a first-born Israelite, seems to be based on older legends from Mesopotamia and Egypt – about the god Horus, for example – none of which were based on fact either. And Moses was never an Egyptian prince. That fragment seems to have come from the story of a Syrian called Bay, who had served as Egypt's chief treasurer, and had made it to Pharaoh as Ramose-khayemnetjeru.

The closer historical research brings us to such subjects, the more, maddeningly, sadly, they seem to dissolve, as if we are obeying some unwelcome form of historical uncertainty principle.

But what is truth? Our modern idea of historical truth – a record as might have been made by an objective recording team on the spot (if true objectivity can *ever* be achieved) – is only one aspect of the deeper importance of history. The Gospel writers certainly saw history differently.

And, after all, the Moses preserved by the myth was a complex, human, inspiring man. He was marked by imperfection: he stammered, and often fell out with the very people he led. He even fell out with his God. But his triumph over those imperfections has been an inspiration to many, over three thousand years. Moses seems irresistible, as vividly real as any personage from 'true' history. Does it *matter* that he never existed?

And what of the future? Can we spot the modern myths and legends which might one day flower into perceived 'truth'?

Our modern world is recorded and documented in extraordinary, unprecedented detail. Some figures, such as British Royals and the children of American presidents, have spent almost every day of their lives in the presence of cameras and microphones. The historians and archaeologists of the future should have much more raw material to work with; indeed it might seem impossible for us to 'forget' as we did in the past.

But great civilisations have fallen before. And it's a chilling thought that an increasing proportion of our culture's collective memory is stored in electronic form, vulnerable to instant destruction by, say, a sufficiently savage solar flare or the electromagnetic pulses of nuclear weapons . . .

New myths will surely sprout from the most stubborn and resonant stories of our time. Think of tales that survive retelling, that in fact benefit from being interpreted anew by each fresh generation: stories of invaders from Mars, of hobbits, of *Star Trek* and *Star Wars*, of Peter Pan, of comic-book heroes like Superman and Batman. It may seem absurd that we could ever 'forget' that these are works of fiction, some of whose creators are still alive today. But Robin Hood began 'life' as a fictional character too.

Perhaps in some atom-blasted future there will be a church based on the worship of a figure born on a far, doomed planet, who fell here as a child, lived in secret among us working mighty miracles with his superpowers, and led us all to a better life by his example. Perhaps the historians of that day, labouring in cathedrals adorned with a mighty golden 'S', will scratch their heads as they wonder if such a place as Krypton ever existed, and if characters like Ma and Pa Kent and Jimmy Olsen are authentic, or embellishments added by later generations of monkish scribes.

Perhaps, like us, they may decide that in the end it doesn't matter: that truth is more than literal. And they will return their precious comic-book fragments – centuries old, gaudy, incomprehensible – to their shrines and arks. But, like us, they will always wonder – and wish they could go back in time and find out.

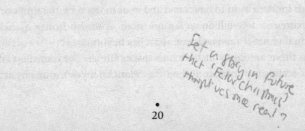

Chapter 3

The Limits of Foresight

The discussions in which we are engaged belong to the
very boundary regions of science, to the frontier where
knowledge . . . ends and ignorance begins.

— William Whewell

The silences in which your minds most often founder
rest well inside your bounderies of knowledge
and feeling.

In later sections of this book, we will peer into the furthest future
we can imagine, times so remote that the universe itself will
become drastically transformed from the warm, bright place we
know. Given the qualifications about forecasting expressed above, it
may seem remarkable, even arrogant, to suppose that we can see so
far. And yet we can, if we make a key assumption: that the laws of
physics will continue to hold, and will remain unchanged, no matter
how far we look into the future. This is only an assumption, but it is
one that appears to hold as we inspect the past, and is therefore our
best guess about the future.

But we must also respect the existence of limits to our understanding. There are boundaries beyond which our science has yet to
cross. As we gaze out at the universe, we can only see stars close
enough for their light to have travelled to us in the time the universe
has existed – ten billion years or more. This horizon expands
continually, but we *cannot* know what lies beyond it.

And there are limits of time and space. On the very smallest of
length scales, for instance (called the 'Planck length'), our physics

theories break down, and we must await a new theory (known as 'quantum gravity', based on a fusion of quantum mechanics and Einstein's relativity) before we can make confident statements. So we should proceed with caution. But much of what we have to say in this book derives from extrapolations well within these limits.

But the Devil is in the detail, and even working within the limits of scientific understanding there are many obstacles in the future to trip the unwary prophet, mainly arising from the discontinuities (like my example of the rise of the motor car) which destroy the existing trends, and immediately make obsolete any prediction based on them.

If there are two areas where such discontinuities lurk, it is in the fields of biotechnology and nanotechnology.

We live in an age of medical miracles, it seems. As the mapping of the human genome progresses – each stage of completeness being reached just a little faster than the results are patented by the world's pharmaceuticals companies – we are promised wonders to come: the conquest of disease and ageing, even the ability to transform our bodies as we desire. We could grow gills, for instance, and start to inhabit the oceans; or perhaps sprout mighty wings and take to the skies . . .

Maybe. But one near-future advance of increasing importance, here in the real world, is likely to be *tissue engineering*. If your liver were to fail it should be possible, in principle, to extract healthy cells from it and 'grow' a healthy new liver from it, to replace the old, and thereby extend the length of your life, and perhaps its quality.

That's the principle. The practice is harder. We can't yet grow organs in a nutrient bath; they need a host body. But if I were to try to grow a liver for you, my immune system would regard it as an invader, and begin the process of destroying it as rapidly as possible.

But this obstacle is being overcome. We have increasing understanding of the workings of the immune system – if only because of diseases like AIDS which damage it, and because of the occasional birth of a 'bubble child', a person born without a working immune system, who must therefore be isolated completely from people and their diseases. The scientists have got as far as producing animals without functioning immune systems, notably mice, and it has proven possible to grow cartilaginous tissue on them. (This is the origin of the rather grotesque images of the mouse with the human ear growing from its back that became notorious some years ago.) But we have yet to grow other forms of tissue successfully – and, of course, a mouse would have some difficulty supporting the growth of a fully formed human liver weighing more than a kilogram.

The physicist and science fiction writer Charles Sheffield has suggested that the ideal site for tissue engineering is one's own body, where the tissue is guaranteed not to be rejected. Sheffield imagines growing copies of his heart, lungs and other organs on or even *in* his own body; when fully grown they would be removed and stored in case of need. It sounds grotesque, but would perhaps be no more inconvenient than a pregnancy – and the potential rewards are great.

If medical science offers us increasing control over our bodies, the new discipline of nanotechnology offers us a still more profound mastery of the material world.

Imagine you could work at the smallest of scales: imagine if you could take apart atoms and rebuild them – turning lead into gold would be a trivial accomplishment – and imagine if you could build machines out of the components of atoms, from electrons and protons. Each tiny machine could achieve little beyond its own scale, but if they could be programmed to work cooperatively they could achieve much more, just as social insects are capable of building structures much more vast and complex than themselves. In fact, if you started with the ability to rewire atoms, then *anything* could be rebuilt from 'the bottom up'.

You could turn waste paper into steak, or water into the finest wine. Nanotechnology offers us an 'anything machine', capable of turning anything into anything else.

These startling concepts date back to a playful 1959 speech by the great physicist Richard Feynman, and were formulated more precisely by Eric Drexler in the 1980s. Drexler imagined self-replicating machines, capable of building copies of themselves from the raw materials around them, and then, having spawned a vast army, going on to work wonders as required.

It seems like a fantastic dream, as if nanotech devices were a fairy dust you could throw into a tub of dirt and watch it being transformed into riches. And the applications Drexler suggested are compelling: flawless quality control, much stronger materials than are available by any other technique, smart machines navigating our bodies and effecting repairs to individual cells, spaceships with hulls of nano-engineered diamond – not to mention the steak.

But all this is *too* wonderful a vision for some sceptics. Nothing in a world ruled by entropy is ever truly flawless; perhaps the perfect replication demanded by nanotech will be forever out of our reach. Further: where will all those tiny machines get their power? And how will they *know* what to do, individually and cooperatively? We have no real idea how to manage the information flows required to sustain Drexler's marvellous visions.

But that is not to say they will not some day come about – and if they do, the world will surely be transformed in ways we probably cannot even envisage today, an authentic discontinuity indeed.

Biotech and nanotech: both these areas of advance are over-hyped at present, and yet they may offer us *complete control* over the stuff of our bodies, and the stuff of the material world around us. If either or both these areas deliver even a fraction of what they promise, they could deliver profound discontinuities; and if we could pass through such a change to its far side, we simple early twenty-first-century folk might wonder if such a change had left our descendants human, as we would understand it.

Nevertheless, having gazed into the abyss of the unknowably strange, we may continue to spin out our predictions for the more distant future. No matter what our command of ourselves and our world, we will still require energy, and will still produce waste, of one form or another; and we will remain bound by the laws of physics and thermodynamics. Of that we are as certain as we are sure of anything.

And as those laws dictate the future of the universe and any possible inhabitants, we may dimly discern the constraints that will operate on our descendants – even if we can never see their faces.

Chapter 4

The Transforming Gadget

> The good effects wrought by founders of cities, law-givers, fathers of the people, extirpers of tyrants, and heroes of that class, extend but for short times: whereas the work of the Inventor, though a thing of less pomp and show, is felt everywhere and lasts for ever.
>
> — **Francis Bacon**

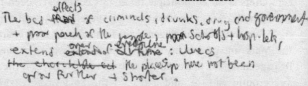

Never underestimate the power of a gadget – the car, TV, the personal computer – to transform the future. Such gadgets are paradigm shifts made solid, and the way to understand their effects is to push their penetration into our lives to the limit, and see what kind of world would result.

One gadget which has already saturated our world in a way few people predicted a few decades ago is the computer. We are seeing consequences, anticipated or not, like the Internet and virtual reality, unimagined not long ago – consequences which may yet go much further, changing our lives, even our very selves.

And it all began with a dream of the Moon.

The Apollo space programme of the 1960s was made possible by a revolution in computing. Computers were needed to guide the great Saturn boosters out of the atmosphere, and to assist Apollo astronauts in guiding their fragile ships to the surface of the Moon.

Apollo's onboard guidance computer seems unbelievably primitive now. It was built around a *core rope*: tiny nickel-iron cores woven together with thousands of copper wires and encased in plastic. The core rope had room for just thirty-six thousand 'words' of memory, and the computer could handle no more than forty-three instructions per second. Programming the system wasn't a question of writing software as we do today; flight software, developed on big IBM mainframes, was *woven* – literally – into the rope.

But the nascent computing industry, given an immense rocket-powered boost by Apollo, reached escape velocity and has never looked back.

It is ironic that the Apollo spacecraft nearly didn't include computers at all; in principle the flights could have been run from giant mainframes at Houston and elsewhere. But the craft were given their own onboard intelligence for two reasons: as preparation for the Mars missions many hoped would follow, where because of lightspeed delays spacecraft would venture far beyond the reach of any ground control; and a fear of the Soviets, and what might become of a lunar spacecraft if nuclear war or sabotage destroyed Mission Control on the ground.

As a boy growing up in the 1960s, I fondly imagined that the next few decades would be dominated by a new generation of spaceships. Instead our era has been shaped, not by the spaceships themselves, but by the clunky electronic gadgets that navigated those ships to the Moon and back.

Today, information technology has transformed our lives at home and at work. And the power of computers continues to increase.

Moore's Law, a pragmatic measurement of the exponential growth in power of computing technology (it doubles every eighteen months), has held good for decades. Some analysts believe this law is soon likely to run out of steam, for we may be approaching the limits of the current technological base. But other possibilities are on the horizon – quantum computing and biotechnological computing to name but two – and I would bet that Moore's Law will continue to work for a long time to come.

The computers are getting very powerful, very fast. What trends can we pick out to help us make sense of the bewildering future they may bring?

Invisible interfaces: Back in the 1960s, computers were so expensive and difficult to use that computing support was available only to highly trained specialists, like astronauts. Even then the systems were hardly user-friendly. During Apollo 11's first lunar landing, the onboard computer began flashing up a warning so obscure that nobody, in the ship or on the ground, could figure it out; the message, which turned out to be harmless, almost led to the aborting of the mission.

Now, computers – cheap and powerful – are to be found in most workplaces and homes in the Western world. And the interface, the window between human and machine, is advancing to the point where it is becoming invisible: far from the impenetrable obscurity of Apollo-style numerical codes, information technology will soon become so easy and intuitive to use that we won't even have to think about it.

Infinite capacity and processing power: There was so little space in Apollo's onboard computers that there were sometimes fist-fights between various subsystem teams as they competed to cram in the data and displays they needed. Today, advances in chip technology are making storage capacity and processing intelligence so cheap that we will soon, perhaps in a decade or two, be able to store and manipulate an arbitrarily large amount of data. We will have *effectively infinite* capacity and processing power.

What will we do with it all?

Imagine a 'Recording Angel': a monitor – light, unnoticed – sitting on your shoulder and transcribing your meetings, your reactions, even (via a neurological link) the evolution of your thoughts, for storage in huge personal databases managed by a descendant of your home computer.

The difference an Angel is going to make to our perception of ourselves is enormous. We have seen that we humans are prone to confabulation, to making up stories about ourselves and the past. For the first time in human history, this kind of unconscious fiction isn't going to be available; in the time of the Angels we're going to have to become used to opening our memories to each other – and to ourselves – with full, uncompromised honesty. A Recording Angel will be immediately useful, for example, in resolving crimes, but it won't necessarily be comfortable to have around.

Intelligent machines: The Apollo computers were pretty dumb. Blindly following its programming, Apollo 11's onboard computer would have landed the ship in a field of boulders, if Neil Armstrong hadn't taken over. Now, advances in processing power are making possible experiments in artificial intelligence which are beginning to challenge our feelings of pre-eminence over 'mere machines'.

Gary Kasparov, the greatest chess player of all time, was beaten in a tournament by a piece of chess-playing software – and not by a mega-suite running on a Cray supercomputer, but by a commercial program sitting on a two-thousand-dollar Pentium-based desktop. Computers have been used to prove mathematical theorems, like the famous Four-Colour Map Theorem: proofs which are already beyond the capacity of individual humans to check out. In financial and other industries, programs which can learn are already proving valuable. Some of these are based on the ideas of 'neural nets' which can evolve rules and make decisions in a flexible way; some use 'genetic algorithms', programs which compete with each other and evolve like living organisms.

Our collective ego took a jolt when primatologist Jane Goodall showed that chimpanzees make and use tools: we humans were no longer distinguished from the world around us by our tool-making. We must prepare for more shocks when the machines reach intellectual peaks, such as in mathematics, which *no* human could hope to emulate.

And maybe they will even start to sing to us.

It is the year 2020, a hot June day. You go for a drive. The car, controlled by the invisible web of satellites far above, accelerates smoothly through a hundred and fifty kilometres per hour, in perfect safety.

You turn on the radio. The station is running a Beatles theme day. The song is 'Maybe I'm Amazed', possibly Paul McCartney's greatest post-Beatles composition, recognisable from the first, faded-in, descending piano chords.

But then the vocals open – and the voice is John Lennon's.

This is not the version you're familiar with, which McCartney, bruised from the band's break-up, recorded in his home studio. This is the Beatles in their mature pomp. Lennon's raw, majestic voice wrenches at the melody, while McCartney's melodic bass, Starr's powerful drumming, and Harrison's wailing guitar drive through the song's complex, compulsive chromatic structure. And then a long coda opens up, underpinned by clean, thrusting brass, obviously scored by the Beatles' great producer George Martin . . .

You listen, mesmerised.

In the 1990s, we were treated to (or subjected to, depending on taste) two 'new' Beatles songs. But the Beatles had broken up twenty-five years earlier. One of their number had actually been dead, sadly, for fifteen years. It seems that breaking up and even death are not necessarily the end of the long and winding road for a classic rock band.

And in the year 2020, you hear, the Beatles are going to be taking to the road for the first time in half a century.

Of course, this will not be the real Beatles. The concerts, indeed the songs, will be an application of virtual reality technology (VR), backed by vast computing power.

Today we associate VR with video games and clunky headsets and gloves, artificial worlds peopled by clumsy cartoon figures. But this is just the modern manifestation, limited only by programming sophistication and computer power. With sufficient power will come arbitrarily good modelling. In fact, in one area, VR technology is already perfect: audio reproduction can now be essentially indistinguishable from the real thing.

So, given arbitrarily powerful computer technology and arbitrarily good VR, how could we generate a Virtual Beatles?

We could easily imagine making VR Beatles mime to old tracks.

We've recently seen new 'Elvis' concerts, recordings of the King playing behind a live band. Meanwhile, much of what we see on movie screens today is entirely artificial, the movie *Toy Story* and its sequel being a classic example. Difficulties in computer-modelling human skin have so far limited the advances made in generating artificial people: watching cartoon Fabs would not be satisfying. But this obstacle will melt away given enough computer power (remember, we're assuming it will be effectively infinite). Probably the first application of this will be a command performance of *Sergeant Pepper's Lonely Hearts Club Band* at the Royal Albert Hall, four thousand virtual holes and all.

But we'll soon tire of watching the V-Fabs miming to old material, however perfectly performed. What about new stuff? What if the Beatles hadn't broken up in 1970? What might their *next* album have been like, if they had recorded their new songs together instead of apart?

Of course John Lennon never sang McCartney's 'Maybe I'm Amazed'. But that's no obstacle. On the 'new' 1990s Beatles' singles, modern recordings were built around 1970s demo tapes of John Lennon's voice.

But you don't need an old tape. We are already familiar with synthesised robot voices, used in applications such as toys, telephone voice-mail, and directory inquiry systems. Granted, these are currently crude, based on reassembled fragments of digitised speech. But this is just a beginning. Voice analysis and recognition software is advancing rapidly. The human voice is a relatively simple instrument. Given enough computing power it is only a small step to modelling a voice, such as John Lennon's, singing a song he never attempted.

But we might be able to go further still.

With a musicological understanding of the Beatles' composition methods, we might even attempt to *rewrite* the solo songs, or even complete unfinished fragments. Experts have attempted to 'complete' Schubert's Unfinished Symphony, and to construct a new Beethoven symphony – his 'Tenth' – from notebooks and extrapolations. Smart enough software could presumably generate *completely fresh* Beatles songs, as they might have been written had the band stayed together until 1972, 1973, 1974 . . .

Philosophers will debate the authenticity of the material. Commentators will bemoan the decline of original music. Fans will download the songs.

Many of the possibilities opened up by virtual reality technology are exciting. In education, for instance. Imagine being able to choose your own virtual tutor – Albert Einstein for physics? And it may be we will go much further. But we must be wary of decadence. VR encourages us to look inward and backwards, and we may become disengaged from the real world. I would enjoy the *Sergeant Pepper* concert, though.

If VR may be an isolating, inward-looking application of computer technology, another may hold the possibility to unite us: indeed to change the world more than we can imagine.

Much of the world is soon going to be online, with Internet access following the mobile phone into ubiquity (indeed these technologies are already merging). I'd predict that seventy-five per cent of the world's population will have some sort of access to the Internet by 2010.

There are very good reasons to believe this: commercial reasons. Already the major supermarkets and other organisations are offering free Internet access in order to promote electronic trading.

Indeed we must hope that online access does become available to all, that economic status is not a barrier. Information access will not only underpin a 'knowledge economy' by supporting lifelong learning: the Internet may also be our best hope for sustaining democracy in the future.

Our democratic institutions, already imperfect, are based on the nation-state; but the nations are increasingly powerless in the face of the immense world-spanning corporate powers spawned by globalisation. For example, in 1999 Microsoft (before its travails with the Justice Department) had a larger 'GDP' than New Zealand. It is not the first time in history that changes wrought by technology and capitalism have run ahead of the capacity of political institutions to keep up, and we are seeing a reaction we have witnessed before: when people feel powerless, they take to the streets.

An ancient science fiction dream (of Gerry Anderson, among others) is of the World Government. Is this what we need to counter the global corporations?

There is a deep suspicion, especially in the United States, of such existing supranational entities as the United Nations, the World Trade Organisation, the International Monetary Fund and the World Bank – and rightly so if they are not transparent and accountable in their workings, and justified by democratic mandate. Perhaps the European Union, which does at least have international institutions which are somewhat democratic, will be seen as a better model for other supranational organisations, an example of how disparate peoples can learn to get along with each other.

But is this any better than handing the world over to the multinationals? Any government controlling vast swathes of the globe is bound to be remote from *me*, the individual voter – isn't it?

Well, perhaps not. Online voting is a simple and easily foreseeable example of the impact of online access. But perhaps the changes will go deeper. As an online citizen, I will become used to participating in the debates which shape my society. I will become empowered. Already, groups of concerned citizens, united online, using the new technology to share information and coordinate their actions, have begun to inspect those who claim power: government bodies, military establishments, corporations.

Perhaps it is unwise to rely too much for our human rights on a piece of technology. But still the Internet, based on universal access, may be our best hope for the accountability which underpins democracy.

And the Internet may even be a force for peace. The Internet is the nearest we have come up with to a machine which allows us to see the other guy's point of view. Perhaps the best hope we have of defeating the evils of the future is our essential human empathy for those we can see and touch – if only by email.

But perhaps the most revolutionary implication of the Internet is not the technology itself, but another application of its design: an application to ourselves.

The computer sitting on your desk is a powerful machine, unimaginably so even a few decades ago. Likewise the computer sitting in your skull is also a powerful beast, far more so than any creation of silicon yet devised. But, as we're learning from the Internet, the real power of computers comes when they are linked together.

Of course even today your brain doesn't operate in isolation; it is connected to other brains through information channels mediated by words, images, sensations. But these channels are limited, grainy, noisy.

Will it ever be possible to link human brains *directly*, to computers and to each other?

The brain, despite its great and still unfathomed complexity, is essentially an information storage system. It holds data as patterns of charge. As such, you would imagine, it must in principle be possible to read off and write to the brain, like any other data store.

Already we have cortical implants which have allowed, for instance, victims of paralysis to control computers by direct instructions from the brain. A recent realisation of this technology is a small glass sphere buried deep in the cortex of a recipient, laced with chemicals; over several months the recipient's neurones grow pathways into the generator and attach themselves to tiny electrodes. Another less invasive approach to reading a brain may be remote sensors of the PET-scan type, which are increasing in power and sensitivity all the time. Eventually we can anticipate a neurone activity pattern analyser, capable of pinpointing individual neuronal synapses as they receive an electrical charge.

Reading a brain, then, seems within reach. *Writing* to a brain may be a little more complex. We know already that memories, for example, are not stored in single locations but seem scattered throughout the brain, in the manner of a hologram. But our understanding is broadening and deepening.

Eventually the technology will come. Perhaps it won't even be necessary to take an implant. You will don a simple headset, no heavier than a pair of glasses, and, by a conscious effort of will, establish a connection from your own brain to a computer.

We have already seen one possible application of this (the Recording Angel). Its application to VR would be spectacular. A direct link between computer and brain would make it possible to model experiences beyond the scope of any external apparatus (for example a bungee jump). You will be able to do anything – for a price.

But we could achieve much more. If we could link brains to computers, then we could link brains to brains: in fact, we could link minds.

What would it be like to be *Joined* – to be part of an Internet of the mind?

In some ways a Joined group will be no more than an extension of our present selves. You are already a set of layers of information processing and function. Some parts of you respond directly, as vegetables do, to simple stimuli: the light-sensitive cells of your retinas, for example. And on top of that there is a higher-order biochemical system of function and control, mediated by the body's fluid flows. When sunlight decreases, your pineal gland produces a complex hormonal message telling your body to prepare for winter.

Animals have evolved, in addition, a central nervous system: information sent as pulses of electrical activity in nerve fibres. This enables you to react more swiftly, and in different ways, because different connection geometries are possible. But the nervous system did not replace the older systems, like the biochemical. Rather the nervous system supplemented what was already there.

Even the crown jewel of your nervous system, your brain, is a thing of layers and substructures. Much of your brain is built on the same suborgans as that of a reptile. Over these ancient designs are laid the more sophisticated mammalian cortex. Your exclusively human pre-frontal lobes are a final addition just a few hundred thousand years old.

And somewhere in the middle of all this multi-layered mesh of networks is *you*, the sum of the parts.

The linking of minds will thus be an extension of the incremental architecture we have inherited from the past: a new layer of processing, superimposed on top of the central nervous systems of each of its members, passing information in a different, faster way.

This will surely be an enhancement of those interconnected, not a diminution. It would be a growth of consciousness – perhaps like the mind-expanding feeling you get when solving a puzzle, or finding the right strategy in a chess game.

If you were Joined, you would no longer be alone. You would share thoughts, feelings, memories. What would it matter if some of those memories were now stored outside your own skull, either in somebody else's head – or maybe in the structure of the higher network itself?

It seems strange to imagine any significant part of yourself stored outside your body. But every day Internet users tap data stores held thousands of kilometres away without even thinking about it.

And we humans already store much information outside ourselves. Think of the tools you use. If you dig your garden, you don't have to invent the spade from scratch: our tools contain the incremental wisdom of their inventors, frozen for all time. The boundaries of yourself are not clear; you are already very blurred.

A Joined group will not be a democracy. But it will not be a dictatorship either, for a Joined network will not be hierarchical. It will be anarchic, chaotic. And it will be robust – perhaps indestructible – for the same reasons the Internet is: if you were to destroy a part of it then the thinking would just find another route and go on.

Perhaps to be Joined will even provide a form of immortality: perhaps copies of yourself, distributed among many heads, could in some sense preserve your identity after your physical death. (But whether that will still be *you* is a question for the philosophers.)

But the Joined will be more than the sum of its parts. Perhaps the Joined will truly be regarded as some new form of mind: a new layer of consciousness, emergent from this new layer of interconnection – a new order of humanity.

We isolated primitives will surely fear these new Joined entities, soon to be emergent among us. But we must try to understand them, for we may need their help in overcoming the dire challenges of the near future.

Chapter 5

Doom Soon?

This is the way I think the world will end – with general
giggling by all the witty heads, who think it is a joke.
— Soren Kierkegaard

This is the way I think the world will begin again –
everything we were never have.
Projecting

I f our divining of the future is to be honest and full, we must
take the bad news with the good, and confront the bleakest of
possibilities.

Prophets like Cassandra, doom-saying daughter of the King of
Troy, have never been popular: nobody likes a party-pooper. But it is
undeniable that one gift of modern science is a knowledge of an
uncomfortably large number of ways in which our world could end
soon: if not the literal destruction of the planet, if not the outright
extermination of mankind (though those unhappy possibilities are
on the table), then at least the smashing of our modern civilisation,
and the relative comfort, health, wealth and large population that go
with it.

But haven't we been assailed by warnings of doom before?

Much science fiction, for example, even while ostensibly about the
future, is moved by the preoccupations of the age in which it was
written: evolution and uncertainty in the 1890s, atomic wars and
their aftermath in the Cold War days of the 1950s, ecological collapse
in the 1960s, and so on. They were stories of futures drawn out in a

straight line from the concerns of that particular decade, and, of course, not all the gloomy forecasts came to pass.

But some of them did.

The science fiction of the first half of the twentieth century was filled with stories of coming European wars, and their dread was justified. That is why our present preoccupations and fears should not be dismissed.

And many people today, surveying the trends of the present, do find much to fear in the near future of the world.

Even a simple list of potential catastrophes is chilling.

We could still obliterate ourselves with war. The traditionally favoured modes, nuclear, biological, chemical, are still with us. Perhaps there are new forms we have yet to glimpse: for example, environmental war.

One disturbing new weapon is the e-bomb, or electromagnetic bomb. The idea is simple: produce a powerful enough flash of microwaves or radio waves and you will fry any electronic circuitry in range. At low powers you could make computers crash; higher powers could panic financial markets, freeze transport, disrupt communications networks. In a world where almost everything we do is dependent on electronic technology, an e-bomb could paralyse a city while causing barely any physical destruction at all.

Such devices are under development, for example for the US Air Force. And there have been persistent rumours that they have already been deployed, by NATO to knock out radar systems during its campaign against Serbia in 1999. But every sword is two-edged; a terrorist, it is said, could cobble together an effective microwave weapon for a few hundred dollars, an e-bomb small enough to fit in the back of a car, powerful enough to crash computers from a hundred metres away. Again there are rumours that such devices have already been deployed, against banks and police operations, in Russia and even London.

But the sophistication of a weapon is irrelevant beside the motivation of its wielder. Every day, machetes, blunt rocks and fists destroy large numbers of irreplaceable human souls, in the brutal, unending conflicts that plague our planet. The twentieth century was by far the worst in human history for deaths in war. And, what is worse, civilian casualties now far outnumber casualties among professional combatants.

Even without malevolence, we can (all too easily) envisage other technological catastrophes.

We might inadvertently set off a genetic engineering disaster, in which a 'green scum' bred for reproductive efficiency overwhelms the biosphere; or we might trigger a human plague, for instance of infertility, arising from some well-meant intervention.

Nanotechnological replicators, capable of reworking matter at the molecular or even the atomic level – a technology often touted as the saviour of the future – could cause almost unimaginable disasters if they got out of hand: for instance, chewing up the whole surface of the planet into 'grey goo', useless copies of themselves.

We can even imagine a 'philosophical' disaster, perhaps linked to a religion. If we began to agree with Schopenhauer who, depressed by evil, wrote that it would have been better if our planet had remained as lifeless as the Moon, it might be hard to get out of bed in the morning.

Beyond such man-made delights, many natural disasters lie in wait. That hoary old favourite, the asteroid strike, is still a candidate; such events have peppered Earth's history, and did, after all, drive a much more ancient animal kingdom than ours – the dinosaurs' – to extinction.

The Earth, it seems, is also overdue for a giant volcanic event, of a scale unseen in all recorded history. The result would be a 'volcano winter' comparable to the aftermath of nuclear war. A much less severe volcanic eruption, in AD 535, prompted a global cooling of the climate, causing extreme weather conditions and disruption to agriculture that led to plagues and population movements, and, it is thought, contributed to the collapse of the Roman Empire in the west.

Perhaps a new Ice Age will be triggered by the Earth's passage through an interstellar cloud – or rather, perhaps the ice will return; we are actually still living through the Ice Age now, enjoying a warm period known as an 'interglacial' between the triumphs of the glaciers. We have survived glaciations before, but it is hard to imagine that our complex modern civilisation could weather such an epochal storm.

There are more outlandish speculations still. The radiation from a nearby supernova could wipe the Earth clean of life; the Earth, in fact, is currently swimming through a bubble in space, blown clear in the interstellar medium by just such an explosion.

Or what about annihilation by extraterrestrials? Perhaps some alien species is busily appropriating the Solar System right now, not even aware that we exist.

Or how about 'vacuum decay'? It seems that space itself, as it unfolded from the Big Bang at the beginning of the universe, is unstable, like a statue standing on a narrow base. It could withstand small disturbances ('small', in this case, includes such things as galactic core explosions) but a powerful enough nudge, properly applied, could cause the whole shebang to tip over into a new form. Such a calamity would be not just the end of the world, but *the end of the universe*.

All of this, to human minds cocooned by thousands of years of comparative climatic and geological stability, seems absurd. Intuitively we feel that the Earth is a stable, infinite, eternal stage for our affairs, and scare stories of disaster, far beyond the scale of the everyday risks we encounter, seem a fitting subject for mockery by the 'witty heads'.

Perhaps this is why we find it difficult to perceive the disasters that are already unfolding all around us.

The impact of the AIDS pandemic on the world, especially Africa, is becoming increasingly well understood.

It is thought that by 2005 twenty-three million Africans will have died of AIDS. In some countries, such as Zimbabwe, one in three of the population is HIV-positive.

Besides the dire cost to human souls, this dreadful culling of young adults is impacting the continent's economic future. Two policemen die of AIDS in Kenya every week; AIDS is the leading cause of death for teachers in the Central African Republic; and so on. Deeper dangers lie further ahead. The CIA has warned that the spread of AIDS in Asia and Africa could trigger ethnic wars and genocide and undermine democratic governments, thereby, says the CIA, threatening US national security, and the rest of the developed world too.

In the middle of the twentieth century, it became accepted wisdom that disease was being beaten back – and indeed some ancient killers have been all but eradicated. AIDS is teaching us that our complacency is misplaced.

We have, after all, been here before. Between 1346 and 1351 about a third of Europe's population was wiped out by bubonic plague – the Black Death. From England to Italy, the effect was devastating, with agriculture and commerce shattered.

Though no sane person would wish for such a disaster, like a fire which clears a space in a crowded forest, the Black Death led eventually to a transformation in Europe's economy. The sudden shortage of labour spurred innovation, as arable land was switched to less labour-intensive pasture, new techniques were developed, fertilisers were spread, and the balance of power between labourers and landowners was changed. But it took more than a century for trade levels to recover to their previous peaks, and two centuries for Europe's population to recover.

Of course our knowledge has greatly advanced since the fourteenth century, and it is possible that the dire future predicated by AIDS can yet be avoided. But it will surely take a huge scientific effort to find a vaccine – and, perhaps, an even greater one of political will to save millions of lives by making it widely available as soon as it is discovered, regardless of the cost. (An organisation called the 'International AIDS Vaccine Initiative' is already campaigning to make this happen.)

But perhaps the true twenty-first-century disaster-in-the-making is simply ourselves – or, rather, the impact we are making on the planet.

Globally there are more people being born on the Earth than are dying: a net gain of *three more people every second*. This seems a frankly remarkable number to me. How are they all to find dignity and purpose?

As we seek to feed and clothe ourselves, we are using up the world and running out of smart ways to use it better. Grain output globally is falling. Farmland is being destroyed by overwork; by 2020 we will lose one-third of today's arable land. Demand for oil will outstrip supply, also projected for the year 2020. We will run out of phosphate in 2050.

Most fundamentally, we are running out of water. Already we humans consume half of all the planet's accessible fresh water. In 1997, for 226 days out of 265, China's Yellow River ran dry before it reached the sea; the farms and factories had taken *all* the water.

And, beyond resource shortages, our very efforts to find more living space for our swelling numbers appear to be having a devastating effect on the planet.

There is now scientific consensus that the Earth's atmosphere is heating up, probably as a result of carbon dioxide emissions. The warming is not just raising sea levels; it is disrupting the Earth's atmospheric and oceanic systems, resulting in extreme weather events including droughts, hurricanes and torrential rain.

At the time of writing, 1998 holds the record for climate disasters, when melting snow killed four thousand people in China, fourteen hundred in India and a thousand in Pakistan. Typhoons killed five hundred people in the Philippines, and monsoons killed thirteen hundred in Bangladesh. Some analysts put the number *already* killed by global warming consequences since 1997 at a hundred thousand. The future is liable to bring further disruption through mass migration as people seek to flee affected areas, more epidemics as viruses jump species barriers, and an increase in poverty and hunger as economies and agriculture are disrupted.

There could even be war. The developing nations produce only twenty per cent of the world's carbon dioxide but suffer the majority of its effects. Perhaps if the developed world remains inactive regarding the problem, this 'carbon aggression' will be met with more direct hostility.

And the long-term consequences could be grave indeed.

The forecasts of future changes in the environment are very uncertain, because the processes – the interaction of living things with the underlying geological and weather processes – are very complex and not well understood. Early computer models of the Earth's atmosphere were regarded as failures, because they kept flipping into one of two stable states: 'White Earth', in which ice sheets cover the whole planet and reflect all the sunlight, and 'Venus', in which a runaway greenhouse effect traps all the sun's heat, the seas boil, and eventually it becomes hot enough to melt lead on the surface.

Now we understand that these are probably Earth's two most *natural* configurations. It is the operation of life, over billions of years, which has maintained the equable atmosphere and temperature conditions we enjoy today. The planet's climate is at best only quasi-stable, like a pencil balanced on its point. We are making large, and unplanned, perturbations . . .

But in the midst of these gloomy projections let us continue to be optimistic. Let's journey again to the year 2100, supposing that Earth has reached a sunnier future. How sunny can this be, and what could we do to make it come to pass?

Today we inject five billion tonnes of carbon dioxide into the air every year. Are there ways to fix this damage?

Perhaps we could collect the CO_2, and bury it underground, maybe in disused oil or gas fields. The North Sea could hold several decades' worth of British CO_2 production. Or the CO_2 could be sunk to the bottom of the ocean: the idea is that under growing pressure, carbon dioxide liquefies. Below three thousand metres, CO_2 dumped into the ocean would form a dense stream and sink to the ocean floor, to be carried away by huge networks of undersea canals or pipes.

Perhaps the CO_2 could be absorbed in extra biomass. All of the

US's current CO_2 emissions could be absorbed by a pond of microalgae, a hundred thousand square kilometres of it. This is practical and cheap, but, since a hundred thousand square kilometres is half the size of Arizona, a little unsightly. A better biomass idea is to reforest. If one-third of the US were reforested, every last tonne of its CO_2 emissions could be absorbed by the trees.

There are more outlandish ideas. According to Walter Seifritz from the University of Stuttgart, we should freeze the CO_2 into gigantic spheres of dry ice. The spheres would be lagged with glass wool, and they would be four hundred metres across – bigger than the Eiffel Tower. You'd need twenty of the spheres per year to absorb Germany's CO_2 output, and Dr Seifritz says they should be sited in all major city centres.

Maybe the trees would be a more attractive solution.

These schemes have drawbacks, not least that most of them end up releasing all the CO_2 into the atmosphere anyway, but on a much longer timescale (centuries), and they'd all require extra energy, which of course would add to the problems, such as heat production, they are supposed to solve in the first place.

Space, the 1950s dream frontier, may after all prove to be the key to the future. We could remove our dirty, heat-making industries – mining, power production – from the environment of Earth, and lodge them in space. Thus we might, conceivably, bring affluence and dignity to all our people, while starting the slow process of healing the planet to the best of our poor understanding and ability. (These possibilities are further explored in Part Two.)

But after a century of such repair efforts, even if successful, Earth will surely seem impoverished. There may be only one species of large mammal left on the planet – humans – save for the pets, and a handful of elephants in a domed preserve in Africa. The Earth will be a huge, managed biosphere, like a park.

And even if technological fixes are available for the environment, we will still face what are called 'closed-economy' problems: like the present battles over the depletion of fish stocks, for instance. Perhaps in 2100 we will be subject to a large degree of central economic control, to manage the diminishing stockpiles. Politically, it may feel to us more like the old Soviet Union than, say, modern America.

I would not wish to trivialise the gravity of our environmental problems. Techno-fix-it schemes are useless unless we address the causes of the problems, and unless we truly understand the environment and the ecology, which are complex, interlinked entities. Quick-fix schemes might even fool us into carrying on polluting without restraint, in the fond belief that somebody is doing something about it.

And I am certainly not arguing that we should run away from our problems – for we cannot.

Over its history Earth has suffered, from a variety of causes, a series of massive extinction events. The asteroid which wiped out the dinosaurs made for a bad day indeed. But the most serious extinction event of all came around two hundred and fifty million years ago, when an estimated ninety-six per cent of all species were destroyed (and we don't know what caused it).

Some scientists argue that the mark we humans are making on our planet can already be classed as a new extinction event.

There is strong evidence that over our history we have forced a series of large mammals into extinction around the planet, through over-hunting and the destruction of habitats. This continues today: some ecologists predict the extinction of two-thirds of *all* bird, mammal, butterfly and plant species by the year 2100. And we make a major impact on Earth's large-scale life-support mechanisms. We humans consume nearly half of the world's *net primary productivity* – the energy trapped by the plants via photosynthesis, the energy required to keep all of Earth's species going.

We humans are hitting Earth with all the impact of the dinosaur-killer comet.

If we are indeed in the middle of a new extinction event, we must recognise that we are not independent of the Earth and its systems; we are intimately bound up in them. *And we cannot escape*, even into space.

There is no conceivable way in the next few decades for more than a tiny fraction – a few thousand perhaps – of Earth's population of *billions* to be taken into space, even supposing there was somewhere for them to go. Most of us, and our children, are going to stay stuck on Earth, and it behoves us to fix the mess we've made. But what we can surely do is to use the immense resources of space to help us through our dangerous century.

And it is important that we do so, that we grasp this opportunity. For it may not come again.

Over the next few decades we will continue to enjoy the (comparatively) cheap energy afforded us by our planet's fossil fuel banks, and we will continue to mine (comparatively) easily accessible resources – and we have the ingenuity to use them. We can use this bounty to heal the Earth, and lay foundations for a long-term future for ourselves – or we might waste it.

But these easy and cheap resources will not last much longer. The average mammalian species has lasted only a few million years; the planet will take much longer to renew the resources we are consuming. Our species *will not* get another chance.

So the twenty-first century is indeed a dangerous century. But it may also be a unique moment in history. If our wisdom does not match our power, if we fritter away this opportunity, future generations will remember what we did, and they will not forgive us.

TWO

•

Into That Silent Sea

Chapter 6

The Stranded Moonwalker

We were the first that ever burst
Into that silent sea.

— Samuel Taylor Coleridge

[handwritten annotation]: We were not the first burst samuel into + cwg from here.

Astronaut Charlie Duke is telling me how the handling of the Apollo lunar lander reminded him of a fighter plane.

'You got a fixed engine to control the ascent, you had these little control jets firing to point you right, and when they fired you went *boom*, and it was fast like this back and forth, it was *bang, bang, bang, bang . . .*' He illustrates his point with vigorous mimes, swivelling his hands sharply left and right, just as the Lunar Module twisted as it rose from the Moon.

It is July 1999, and we're having lunch in a hotel in Bond Street, London. In 1972 Charlie Duke, the Lunar Module Pilot of Apollo 16, made, with John Young, the fifth successful Moon landing. Today Duke is a dapper sixty-three-year-old, brought here by a watch corporation to promote its thirty-year association with the American space programme.

'It was like being a rough acrobatic pilot. Oh, great ride. But the Lunar Module goes straight up for eight hundred feet and then pitches over to accelerate into orbit. And the horizon disappears out the top of the window. So now you're just looking down at the ground and it's a vertigo feeling that you're going to do this . . .' His hand plunges back into an imaginary lunar surface.

It is easy to forget that human beings have already walked on the surface of another world.

You probably remember the name of the first man to walk on the Moon: Neil Armstrong, of course. Perhaps you even remember the second, Buzz Aldrin. The name of Jim Lovell, commander of ill-fated Apollo 13, sticks in the mind, thanks largely to the Hollywood movie. Lovell never walked on the Moon, but ten more men did after Armstrong and Aldrin. Who was the third, the fourth, the last?

It's remarkable that most of the Moonwalkers – twelve men who went through perhaps the most extraordinary human experience of the second millennium – have become largely anonymous. Space is an age-old dream, and, as we will see, is a hard-headed prospect for the future of our species. And yet humanity's single bold space adventure is receding into the past, already so distant that more than half the people alive today don't even remember it.

It might have been very different: building on the successes of Apollo, Americans might already have reached Mars. But they didn't. What can we learn for the future from this vivid episode of the recent past?

In all there were just six successful Moon landings, carrying two astronauts each to the lunar ground. Apollo 11, crewed by Neil Armstrong and Buzz Aldrin, was the first to achieve a landing, in July 1969. Three Apollo missions reached the Moon without completing a landing: two rehearsal flights (Apollos 8 and 10) and the ill-fated Apollo 13. Of the men who flew these flyby missions, two (John Young and Gene Cernan) would eventually walk on the Moon and one, Tom Stafford, would later fly an Earth-orbit Apollo mission. But for three of these voyagers, their lunar flyby was their only space-flight, and one man, Jim Lovell, was fated to fly on both Apollos 8 and 13 without ever setting foot on lunar soil.

None of the twelve Moonwalkers returned to the Moon for a second trip, though two of them, Pete Conrad and Alan Bean, would fly later on Skylab, and John Young went on to pilot the Space Shuttle. For the rest, their lunar voyage was their last journey into space.

Indeed, remarkably, for four of the Moonwalkers the Moon trip was their *only* spaceflight – including Charlie Duke.

'Up until that point I was basically non-stop talking, feeding them information. But then I realised, be quiet, let 'em land. But what's going through my mind is I don't understand what's happening . . .'

In July 1969 Duke worked in Mission Control at Houston as capsule communicator (capcom) to Apollo 11 during Neil Armstrong's landing. At the last minute Armstrong realised the computer was flying him into a lethal boulder field and he took over the controls, but he had no time to tell Mission Control why.

'I mean he was flying across the lunar surface at about four hundred feet. Finally we see him pitch back, slow down and then start down on descent. And that's when, because of this overfly, we were running out of gas.'

When Apollo 11 completed its landing in the Sea of Tranquillity, with just a few seconds' hovering time left in its fuel tanks, the human race began to breathe again – as Duke reported to Armstrong at the time, as his voice became the first to be heard by humans on the Moon.

Three years later it was Duke's turn.

On the far side of the Moon Apollo 16 burned its engines to enter lunar orbit. 'We were in darkness at that point. Then just seconds after the engine shut down – wham, sunlight. There's no sunrise glow, like on Earth – there's no atmosphere – so it's just wham, there's daylight. The shadows were real dark, real deep, and it looked rough.' But he doesn't remember looking out to see the glow of his engines on the rocks of the Moon. 'Your gaze is on the instruments because it's critical you do the right thing. A one second overburn would impact you on the surface.'

A day later, in the Descartes region of the lunar highlands, Charlie Duke walked on the Moon. His account of his stay on another world is full of a pilot's precise observational detail, couched in homespun language.

'You couldn't feel the texture of the rock. You couldn't feel it under your feet either. You sank into the dust. In some areas you sank in half an inch, some were deeper than that. There were no colours, just shades of grey. As you looked away from the sun, it was a very light grey. The more you turned into the sun the darker the grey became. The texture: if you've ever seen a freshly ploughed field, harrowed and very fine, and you know how when it rains on it, it gives you that sort of pimply look . . . That was how it was. But it was dry as toast.'

At the climax of their exploration Duke and Young drove up a steep lunar mountain, reaching the greatest altitude of any lunar astronauts. 'Incredible. Out to the horizon was just rolling terrain as far as you could see, mostly light grey. You could see the Lunar Module sitting out in the centre of the valley and our single track leading up to us. It was very dramatic.'

After Apollo, Charlie Duke stayed with NASA for three more years working on Space Shuttle designs. But he grew bored. 'The Shuttle was just a big space truck. It couldn't compare with flying to the Moon.' So he accepted an offer to go into business with a friend. 'I went from the Moon to money, if you will.' Now retired, he finds much consolation in his Christian ministry. But he regrets the brevity of his adventure. 'After Apollo I was hoping that certainly by now we'd go to the Moon again, or we'd go to Mars, but now it's all refocused to Earth orbit, the big Space Station, so I think it's gonna be quite a time before we get a chance to go back.' Briefly he looks lost, uncomfortable.

In 1972 Charlie Duke was only thirty-six, and he might indeed have gone on to Mars.

After the lift-off of Apollo 11 in July 1969, an exuberant Vice-President Spiro Agnew proclaimed that the US 'should articulate a simple, ambitious, optimistic goal of a manned flight to Mars by the end of the century'. And NASA had strong, feasible plans to achieve that goal. America has never been so close again to assembling the commitment to go to Mars.

What went wrong?

The Apollo era was born in 1961. Just a week after Soviet Yuri Gagarin's pioneering first spaceflight in April, President Kennedy sent a memo to Vice-President Johnson asking for options. 'Do we have a chance of beating the Soviets by putting a laboratory in space, or by a trip around the Moon, or by a rocket to land on the Moon, or by a rocket to go to the Moon and back with a man? Is there any other space programme which promises dramatic results in which we could win . . . ?'

There was no overriding logic favouring a Moon goal. NASA even looked at going to Mars *first*, with nuclear rockets. And in private, Kennedy berated his technical advisers for not producing recommendations for more tangible, down-to-Earth scientific spectaculars, such as desalinating sea water.

So when Kennedy made his famous 1961 commitment to put a man on the Moon within a decade, the new programme was not intended as a first step into space. It was a political gesture. Technically Apollo was an end in itself, a system designed to place two men on the Moon for three days, and it did just that. Its political goals were to beat the Soviets in space, and it did that too. After Apollo, there was no political or technical inertia to be carried forward to future goals.

And meanwhile the next logical goal, Mars, had proven itself to be a disappointment. The first unmanned probes showed it to be, not Earth-like, but a desolate cratered place, like the Moon.

Suddenly Mars wasn't worth the cost of the trip.

In February 1969, a few months before the first Apollo Moon landing, the incoming Nixon Administration appointed a Space Task Group (STG), chaired by Vice-President Agnew, to develop post-Apollo goals for NASA. Agnew himself was a champion of going to Mars, even though he was booed when he spoke about it in public.

The final STG report, as delivered to President Nixon in September 1969, proposed a series of 'common elements': a shuttle, a space station, a space tug, nuclear rockets, and a Mars Excursion Module.

The modules could be put together into a series of mission profiles to achieve a variety of goals.

NASA knew exactly how it would fly to Mars.

The earliest Mars mission would have left Earth on 12 November 1981, consisting of two nuclear-boosted ships each carrying six men. On arrival at Mars in August 1982, the astronauts would descend in Apollo-style landers for a surface stay of thirty days. The return trajectory would feature a velocity-shedding swing past Venus. The expedition would return home on 14 August 1983, and the astronauts be brought back to Earth by shuttles. (It is eerie to study the yellowing plans of such missions today, littered with dates now lost deep in the past.)

It was a beautiful dream. But public and political reactions were swift and negative.

The America of 1969 – at war in Vietnam, riven by social division at home – was a very different place from 1961. There was no perceived threat to provide the necessary political impetus behind a new programme. In 1961 Kennedy had been promoting the space programme as part of a greater technological solution to the perceived threats and problems: eliminating poverty, resisting Communist expansion, promoting development abroad. In fact only a fifth of Kennedy's famous May 1961 speech had been devoted to spaceflight. While there was no doubt that NASA itself was an astonishing success, by 1969 technology had clearly failed to build a better world – indeed, there was a great suspicion of the 'military-industrial complex' against which Eisenhower had warned.

President Richard Nixon seemed to understand the anti-techno-cratic mood of his day. In March 1970 Nixon formally responded to the STG report. His language was cautious. 'We must . . . recognise that many critical problems here on this planet make high priority demands on our attention and our resources . . . With the entire future and the entire universe before us . . . we should not try to do everything at once. Our approach to space must continue to be bold – but it must also be balanced.'

Out of all the STG's grand vision, Nixon chose only the Space

Shuttle. Anything else was just too expensive. It was a crucial moment which has shaped manned spaceflight ever since.

During his journey home, with Apollo 16 suspended between Earth and Moon, Charlie Duke assisted in a space walk to retrieve instrument records.

'As I floated out, the Earth was off to the right, probably about a two-o'clock low, real low. I could see it beyond the hatch, beyond the Service Module. And it was just a little thin sliver of blue and white. And then I spun around this way and directly behind me there was this enormous full Moon, and it was, I mean it was overwhelming, that kind of feeling. And you could see Descartes, you could see Tranquillity, all the major features, and it just felt you could reach out and touch 'em. No sensation of motion at all. The sun was up above my eye line but it's so bright you don't look at it. And everything else was just black.

'There was more of a feeling of being in an audience as you were floating. Here was this big panorama in front of you, below – I just sort of felt detached, I was just enjoying the view, as if I was enjoying the play . . .' His eyes shine as he mimes for me his spacecraft, once more suspended between Earth and Moon and sun.

Charlie Duke is a peculiar modern phenomenon: the stranded Moonwalker, granted just three remarkable days on the Moon and then doomed to tell his story over and over, for the rest of his life. But still, even after years of retelling, his joy at his adventure shines through.

In assessing NASA's future, given the circumstances of the time, President Nixon was probably right in his decision. But in the end, we cannot help but regret the loss of the great spectacle we should have enjoyed had Charlie Duke walked on Mars in 1982.

Chapter 7

Obsolete Dreams

Round the decay
Of that colossal wreck, boundless and bare
The lone and level sands stretch far away.

— Percy Bysshe Shelley

[handwritten margin notes:]
Bob to Nine Plates
in bar when
asks
question
for free
drink.

Space
Spacing up
your
to that pony future, obsolete + bare,
And most of the universe might join you.
talks *give up ~ Rebirth at Farewells*
to give *the bare*
you

I t's a hot early morning in July 1995. We're in the Kennedy Space Center press stand. We are looking east, into the sun. Before us is a TV monitor, but we can see nothing in the glare.

The huge Vehicle Assembly Building is to our left. There is a patch of grass before us, with the press Portakabins, and a big rectangular digital clock, counting down, and a flagpole. Then there's a stretch of water – the barge canal from the Banana River, along which the engineers haul bits of rocket booster to be assembled. Then, beyond a treeline straight ahead of us, there are two launch complexes: 39-B to the left, loaded with Space Shuttle *Discovery*, and 39-A to the right, with *Endeavour*. *Discovery* is to be launched today. 39-A is the old Apollo Moon rocket gantry. 39-B launched *Challenger*. In fact *Discovery*'s cargo today replaces a cargo lost on *Challenger*.

To the right, there are more pads, stretching off to the south. Many of these are now disused, dismantled, literally museum pieces.

In the early mist, the launch complexes look grey, colourless, like bits of an oil refinery. But when the mist burns off I can see the gleaming white of the Shuttle orbiter against the orange External

Tank and the battleship grey of the gantry. The orbiter looks astonishingly beautiful, like a 1950s vision of a spaceplane.

Launch is due at 9:41 a.m.; it is fifty-five seconds late.

At main engine start, a bright light erupts at the base of the orbiter, and white smoke squirts out to either side. Then the stack lifts off the ground, startlingly quickly, trailing a column of smoke which glows orange within, as if on fire. The plume of yellow light from the solid rocket boosters is incredibly bright – not like the TV pictures, almost dazzling, like sunlight, liquid light. The stack arches over onto its back and follows a steep curve away from its tower. Already the gantry is dwarfed by the smoke column.

The sound starts to reach us after ten or fifteen seconds. I don't feel the gut-wrenching people often describe, but it's no ordinary noise: a cracking, thundering sound which comes tumbling down at us from the sky above our heads. These are shock waves from the engines, nonlinear wave fronts collapsing and interacting, very sharp thunderous slaps over an underlying rumble.

I can hear people applaud. I whoop myself; it is a very joyous moment, even for battered old hacks in the press stand; a very physical, immense event, a huge release of energy.

The stack climbs right up into the sun: a poignant scene, the smoke column arching up into the sun, writhing in the breeze. So we miss the last visible event, the solid rocket booster separation, in the glare. But we stay in our seats through ten minutes or so, to follow the crew to orbit.

The smoke column is still there, slowly dispersing and growing more ragged, kilometres wide, when we drive away.

This is the US space programme today.

There's no doubt that the Space Shuttle, one of mankind's two (count them) operational manned spaceship designs, provides a magnificent spectacle. But the Shuttle is an ageing system, born of political and financial compromises in a very different era, and, as it strives to meet the challenge of the construction of the International Space Station, it is a system riddled by flaws that might yet lead it to fresh disaster.

And a key element in the design compromises was that the Shuttle was intended to be, not a vehicle to deliver the colonisation of the Solar System, but a military spaceplane.

For fifty years the US Air Force (USAF) has lobbied for a place at the heart of space war planning. The result has been a remarkable, and for a long time clandestine, parallel US space programme.

The military potential of space was obvious early. From the end of the Second World War, presidents from Truman onward planned to use missiles and bombers to contain the USSR, and they understood how the information provided by reconnaissance satellites would make another Pearl Harbor impossible. By the end of the 1950s the USAF had taken delivery of its first intercontinental ballistic missile (ICBM), the Atlas, and in 1960 its first reconnaissance satellites went live.

And it looked as if the first steps towards military manned flights into space had already been taken. On 14 October 1947, Chuck Yeager flew the rocket plane X-1 past Mach One and into history. In July 1954 the X-15 project was initiated: a new rocket aircraft capable of reaching Mach Six and a hundred thousand metres. All this research would lead logically to a manned, practical, winged reusable space vehicle: wings into space.

In 1951, the USAF began work on the secret 'Bomi' (Bomber-Missile) project. It was a spaceplane that would ride piggyback on a mother ship, reaching Mach Twelve at an altitude of sixty kilometres, and glide around the world to deliver its atomic bomb.

The Bomi remained a paper study, beyond the reach of available technology. But it led to a new spaceplane project, the X-20 spaceplane. The X-20 would have been boosted to Mach Eighteen by a Titan ICBM.

Meanwhile, throughout the 1950s, the USAF had been thinking further – a lot further.

They even planned nuclear missile silos on the Moon! This was seen as a logical extension of the Mutual Assured Destruction strategy. The Soviets would have to launch an overwhelming nuclear attack on the Moon two or three days before attacking the US – or else attack the US first, only to receive 'sure and massive destruction' from the Moon two days later . . .

Such terrifying visions were not put aside until 1967 when the Outer Space Treaty was signed, banning bombs in space.

Everything changed for the US space effort on 4 October 1957, when a Soviet ICBM launched Sputnik 1 to orbit, the first artificial Earth satellite.

The military value of space was clear to President Eisenhower, but in the wake of Sputnik he felt that the US space programme ought to appear open and honest, in contrast to the USSR's sabre-rattling. Thus, civilian NASA was set up to manage the space effort. It was a crucial blow to the ambitions of the Air Force.

And then, on 12 April 1961, the Soviets launched Yuri Gagarin into orbit, in a simple ballistic capsule. A month later, President Kennedy committed the nation to landing men on the Moon before 1970. For a decade, the USAF was eclipsed by NASA's Mercury, Gemini and Apollo successes.

But after Apollo ended, the balance of space power between civilian and military began to shift.

Those who founded NASA, and drove it all the way to the Moon, shared a dream of the future in space.

This dream was most clearly articulated by Wernher von Braun, the German engineer who led rocket development projects from the V-2 to Saturn V. Though in recent years his reputation has been tainted by revisionist views of his complex relationship with the Nazi regime, there can be no doubt about von Braun's contribution to space technology. *All* the rocket systems operated today by both the US and Russia trace their ancestry back to the V-2. And von Braun's vision of the future in space beyond the Moon, communicated to the public in a series of publicity efforts in the 1950s and 1960s, was plausible, authoritative and compelling.

The key would be a series of space stations in low Earth orbit. Connected to the surface of the Earth by shuttle craft, these great platforms would provide services to the Earth – for example, gathering solar power – and would serve as ports for great exploratory spaceships. In a series of sketches of increasingly greater sophistication von Braun and his colleagues imagined modular systems in which nuclear rockets would be assembled for a variety of purposes, reaching to the Moon, Mars and beyond. This inter-planetary step-ladder scheme is roughly the vision dramatised in the Clarke–Kubrick classic movie *2001: A Space Odyssey*, with its clipper ships and wheel-shaped space platforms.

And in the 1960s it was no peripheral view. As noted in Chapter 6, the von Braun step-ladder vision formed the foundation of recommendations made in 1969 to President Nixon as he sought input on the way forward for NASA after Apollo. Many in NASA hoped that after the 'diversion' of Apollo – which was essentially a dead-end system with no purpose save for delivering the Moon landings – the 'true' future could be built, with a multi-purpose extendable system that might take America back to the Moon and much further.

But, for a complex of political, cultural and financial reasons, the grandiose step-ladder vision was finally rejected by Nixon. The one element picked out for development was the Space Shuttle. It is entirely possible, in fact, that US manned spaceflight might at this point have been terminated altogether; it was only because a linger-ing belief that a nation like America should be able to afford some-thing more than welfare programmes that any of it survived at all.

But the Shuttle's role in the step-ladder scheme was to have been as a mere space truck, transporting astronauts and supplies to and from the great space stations and interplanetary rockets. There would be no stations or missions to Mars for a while yet: without anywhere to go, what would the Shuttle be *for*?

Military strategists saw an opportunity. As NASA scrambled to devise science programmes and unambitious construction projects to be run from a low-Earth-orbit reusable spacecraft, the USAF began to propose new jobs for the orphaned Shuttle – working for the military.

The plan was that the USAF would have its own spaceplanes. Two of five planned orbiters would be based at the USAF's own Shuttle assembly and launch facility at Vandenberg, flying up to twenty military missions a year, launching reconnaissance and hunter-killer satellites, serving as a platform for space-based weapons, and even capturing enemy satellites.

But civilian and military interests in the Shuttle project were in conflict. The USAF wanted a high-performance Shuttle with a large carrying capacity and high 'cross-range' capability – that is, an ability to vary landing sites widely. But NASA also had to meet its commitment to make access to space more economical.

In 1970 the base assumption had been that the Shuttle would be a two-stage, fully reusable system with both stages piloted and capable of landing on a runway like a conventional aircraft. Soon the idea of a flyback first stage was dropped, leaving a much smaller single-stage spaceplane with a smaller payload, a throwaway propellant tank and strap-on, solid-rocket boosters: much cheaper to develop, but much more expensive to fly – and far more dangerous.

Unlike liquid-fuel rockets like Apollo's Saturn V, solid rocket boosters are giant firecrackers: once lit, they can't be turned off. Before the Shuttle, no human had ever flown on a solid rocket, and many of NASA's astronauts were deeply concerned, even so early, about the Shuttle's safety (and it was, tragically, a solid rocket booster flaw that caused the fatal *Challenger* disaster of 1986).

The Shuttle finally flew, much delayed, in 1981, piloted by Charlie Duke's Apollo 16 commander John Young.

The first all-military Shuttle payload, a satellite, was carried in July 1982. There was even rumoured to be a dry 'bomb run' from orbit over Moscow.

But the Shuttle was far from an unmitigated success for the USAF, proving expensive and prone to delays.

And then in January 1986 came the *Challenger* disaster, and the grounding of the Shuttle.

After *Challenger*, emergency procedures were reviewed, and NASA strove mightily to close what it calls the 'non-survivable windows' in the Shuttle flight profile. Shuttle astronauts now have a range of abort and safety options available through their mission, particularly in the most dangerous phase, the launch to orbit.

The Shuttle, with a new orbiter to replace *Challenger*, returned to service, of a sort, in 1988, and has flown steadily ever since.

Now the Shuttle is coming under more pressure than before, as it is called on to make dozens of flights in support of the construction and manning of the new International Space Station. At the same time, NASA privatised Shuttle operations in 1998, and in search of economy the overall Shuttle workforce has been cut. Although NASA insists no compromises have been made in safety, some observers have warned of an erosion of safety levels.

After *Challenger*, NASA engineers evaluated the risk of losing another orbiter on a given launch as about one in two hundred. The Shuttle's compromised design has always made it an intrinsically risky system; it seems unlikely the risk level can be engineered much lower.

One in two hundred: with every flight the Shuttle makes, the Russian roulette continues. NASA and its industry partners are exploring options for an eventual Shuttle replacement, but with each passing year – and new rounds of budget-trimming – that prospect grows more and more remote, and a number of re-engineering initiatives are underway to extend the life of the existing system for *decades*.

For the foreseeable future, barring calamity, the Shuttle will continue to be the bedrock of the US manned space programme: this ageing space truck born out of a compromise, as Space Age dreams were remoulded in a Cold War crucible.

Shuttle mission 51C, in January 1985, was the first fully secret USAF mission. Even the launch could not be shown live. One former astronaut sourly remarked as he watched the launch that this was the day Americans should have been going to Mars . . .

Space dreamers in the United States and the Western world long to believe that the end of Apollo decision-making was an opportunity missed, but not an irreversible defeat. But Mars may not wait for America for ever: history teaches us that opportunity does not always strike twice.

Like the Americans, the Chinese have been through a great exploration phase. They too turned back. If they had not, the world would be a very different place.

Once, the Chinese led the world in technology: they had printing, gunpowder, the compass, in some cases centuries before Europe. And at the time of the early Ming Dynasty, in the early fifteenth century, they went exploring.

Under the authority of Emperor Yung-Lo, a Yunnanese Muslim eunuch called Zheng Ho assembled a great exploratory navy. The first westward expedition set off in 1405. (By comparison, the first of the great Portuguese voyages of discovery, under Prince Henry, would not take place until 1420.) The Emperor's purpose was expansion: the expeditions were to serve as a precursor to a new network of trading relationships.

The Chinese vessels were 'treasure ships', the biggest a hundred and fifty metres long and weighing fifteen hundred tonnes. The ships, equipped with compasses and watertight compartments, were decades ahead of anything the Western powers could build, and the size of the flotillas was much bigger than their later Portuguese equivalents. Zheng Ho's very first expedition, which reached India, included sixty-two vessels carrying twenty-eight thousand men.

In all, between 1405 and 1433, Zheng Ho made seven westward voyages. Chinese explorers reached Hormuz at the throat of the Persian Gulf, Aden at the mouth of the Red Sea, rounded southern Asia to Bengal, and even, in 1420, reached the east coast of Africa, fifty years ahead of the Portuguese. The ships brought home exotic novelties – people, animals, plants – and struck terror and awe wherever they landed.

Had the Chinese continued, they could surely have forestalled the Portuguese in taking possession of Hormuz and in rounding the Cape of Good Hope; and they could have anticipated the Spaniards in discovering and conquering the Americas. Perhaps today we would remember Zheng Ho rather than Columbus . . . China's Middle Kingdom could, perhaps, have come to embrace the world.

But none of this happened, for the Chinese turned back.

In 1436 a new Emperor, called Zheng Dung, came to the throne. He cut the building of ships and the construction of armaments. The great navy fell apart, and China was once more isolated from the rest of the world until the barbarians from Europe came sailing in four centuries later.

Just like the Americans in the 1970s, internal politics had cut short the great Chinese adventure.

There was intense conflict between the Confucian scholars who ran the imperial bureaucracy and the Grand Eunuchs of the Imperial Court. The Eunuchs' voyages were seen as a threat to the bureaucracy. But the Confucians were in charge of educating the new Emperor, and they had played a long game. They had convinced the young Zheng Dung that China, affluent and self-sufficient, didn't need to deal with the barbarian lands at its rim.

So, to maintain their power, the bureaucrats blocked technological development, the explorers were recalled, and an historic opportunity was lost.

We can't say what kind of world the Chinese might have built if they had continued. Chinese technological development, already far ahead of the West, would surely have been accelerated by the opening up of new frontiers. Perhaps a Chinese history would have surpassed the achievements of our own civilisation.

And, remember, the Chinese had already been studying rocketry for centuries. Who's to say that some spiritual descendant of Zheng Ho, perhaps born in a Chinese America, might not have initiated space exploration decades – even centuries – ahead of our own schedule?

Perhaps, when the Emperor called back Zheng Ho, the Chinese lost more than one world.

The universe will not wait until we are ready; there is no inevitability to history. It's possible that our Western civilisation has already missed its chance to reach for the new worlds in the sky, that others will soon overtake us, and that in five centuries our descendants will rue our lost opportunity, just as some Chinese today must rue the recall of Zheng Ho and his fabulous treasure ships.

Chapter 8

Heaven and Earth

Hitch your wagon to a star.

— **Ralph Waldo Emerson**

Bob to Martha who wants
to navigate his ship
' Hitch your own wagon to a star!')

What has space ever done for you?

Space travel strikes many people today as a dream of a vanished technocratic age: overblown, over-expensive, over-hyped. Certainly space travel has not delivered all it promised to me as a wide-eyed boy in 1965, dreaming of holidays on the Moon, bases on Mars, and brave astronauts venturing out to Jupiter's moons.

But the near future of manned spaceflight, locked up in the giant, hugely expensive International Space Station, seems assured. And meanwhile space shapes all our lives in immeasurable ways.

We are drenched by space spin-offs.

Airline pilots, yachtsmen, polar explorers and even the pilots of hot-air balloons now routinely check their position, receive weather information and contact home base with the help of satellite networks. The development of smart miniaturised machines may lead to the launch of thousands of small, cheap 'nano-satellites' that will cover the Earth like a cloud, allowing truly global access to communications systems.

Meanwhile, satellites monitoring such climatic indicators as the height of waves in polar seas, the El Niño storm system and the ozone layer holes are contributing to powerful new models of the world's weather. Measurements of soil moisture changes can predict famines before they happen. Ground-penetrating radar instruments can even see through the Earth, detecting underground rivers and archaeological treasures.

And the spin-offs of space research continue to filter into our global economy, largely unnoticed.

Detectors devised by astronomers to study the most remote and faint of objects may be used to monitor cancer cells as they form; space telescope technology has revolutionised breast biopsy by removing the need for conventional surgery. Space hardware – and software – must operate under extreme conditions: accelerated to eight kilometres a second for launch, and then subject to airlessness, ferocious extremes of heat and cold, and a lethal drenching of radiation, perhaps for years. Addressing such problems has led to significant payoffs in robotics, data handling, sensor technologies and material sciences.

Space materials have been used in lightweight cycle helmets, baby prams, scratch-proof watch glasses and spectacle lenses, and air bags and lubricants in cars. Even the training shoes on your feet may incorporate Moon-boot materials to improve shock absorption, grip and stability.

But there are many voices in the US and beyond who want to see less benign spin-offs: an expansion of military ventures in space.

Space war sounds like science fiction. But we have seen that planners in the USAF have been considering space war futures for fifty years, and already one real-world conflict – the Gulf War – has been powerfully influenced by space systems.

In September 1982, the USAF's Space Command was created by combining missile, warning and space operations. But the USAF has since undergone a major rethink of its structure and role, forced on it by the ending of the old Cold War polarity, the advance of technology, and, in the 1990s, by funding reductions.

The USAF's new space mission is rooted in the concept of the 'extended battlefield'. Combat will take place, so the theory goes, not just at the front but deep within the enemy's territory, with the interdiction of the movement of troops, supplies and information. This requires close air and land coordination. Information support, provided by unmanned space systems, has a central role.

In 1991, Operation Desert Storm was the first big test of this concept, as Air Force satellites were heavily used in the successful information war against Saddam.

Today Space Command, employing forty thousand people, operates forty-five satellites and launches one a month. Space Command operates hundreds of Minuteman III and Peacekeeper ICBMs. Space Command's surveillance satellites include Keyhole photography satellites, Magnum phone-tappers, LACROSSE radar imagers, Project White Cloud ship watchers, Jumpseat electronic transmission monitors. Navstar satellites are the backbone of the Global Positioning System for worldwide navigation. Milstar communications and Defence Support warning satellites hover in geosynchronous orbit over trouble spots.

Meanwhile the USAF – as it always has, it seems – is thinking ahead to the space wars to come.

The Air Force Weapons Laboratory in Albuquerque researches space-based lasers, weapons that attack other satellites, and re-entry warhead vehicles to attack hardened bunkers. The Phillips Laboratory in New Mexico is developing satellites called TAOS – Technology for Autonomous Operational Survivability – smart enough to operate independently in the event of war, and maybe even to continue the fight from space. The first test TAOS was launched in March 1994.

Meanwhile, the Americans have been experimenting with ASATs (anti-satellite systems) since 1959. In September 1985, a USAF F-15 made a high-speed climb and launched a missile into space to shoot down a test satellite. But in 1988 the ASAT programme was cancelled as being 'destabilising'.

For now these schemes are restricted to low-Earth orbit; for now nobody is considering, or funding, a return to dreams of nuclear weapons on the Moon. But some thinkers continue to venture further. One analyst wants space battle stations at the stable Lagrange orbital points to command the Earth–Moon system.

And even now the cost is huge. Up to Desert Storm, the US spent two hundred billion dollars on space warfare systems. That would pay for *five* Apollo Moon programmes.

But military space efforts should not be dismissed as mere technocratic warmongering: we may be better off with the space warriors than without them. President Eisenhower's dream of 'Open Skies', in which the territory of enemies is opened for inspection by surveillance satellites, has surely led to stabilisation of relations and a reduction of conflicts.

The benefits that flow to Earth from space have come almost by accident.

After all, space programmes are not *for* spin-offs. The first space programmes were spawned out of the Cold War. The Soviet Union used orbital exploits to establish a new image for itself as no longer primitive and agricultural, but an advanced technological nation capable of competing with the Americans; the US needed to respond to repair the damage.

Now the world looks very different. The USSR has collapsed, and so the rules of the game have changed. As a result, we have seen a remarkable convergence of the once-competing American and Russian manned space programmes.

In December 1993 the Russians were formally invited to join the International Space Station project (ISS), which at that time included the US, Canada, Japan, and members of the European Space Agency. The new project has three phases. Phase One involved rendezvous missions of the Shuttle and the existing Russian Mir Space Station. In Phases Two and Three, a new international space station will be constructed and operated. The station will need nineteen Shuttle launches and twelve Russian booster launches before completion.

(On a research trip to NASA's Johnson Space Center in Houston I got to explore the big, full-size station trainer facility they've built there. It was a set of cylinders the size of school buses, fixed at right angles to each other; it felt a bit like climbing through a huge central heating system.)

But why should we build the Space Station at all?

As noted in the last chapter, NASA, led by the visions of Wernher von Braun, has been campaigning for space stations since the 1960s. The current scheme is a remote descendant of a proposal accepted by President Reagan in 1984. Unlike 1969, the 1984 scheme saw no wider programme of Solar System colonisation with the station as a hub; the stated goals were concerned with science, industrial research and so on. But the station's true objective was unstated: the whole thing was a show of US leadership at a time of belligerence towards the Soviets.

In the Gorbachev era, the Cold War justification went away, and the Space Station became just another high-cost super-science boondoggle, one of many vying for funding in Congress. The latest station scheme is actually a smart reworking of those earlier proposals; by making the station a showcase of *cooperation* with the Russians, the Clinton Administration introduced a new raison d'être for the project – a complete inversion of the station's original Cold War justification!

In the best tradition of the space programme, the emphasis is still on hardware and politics, not needs and uses: in December 1994, the General Accounting Office, Congress's investigative arm, pointed out that NASA's budget was so stretched by the Space Station project that NASA had only a third of the researchers it needed to achieve the station's scientific goals.

But there *is* much good science to be done in Earth orbit: the study of plant growth, human physiology and crystal structures in space will help scientists understand the influence of the gravity field within which we are all embedded – for example, research on the Mir space station may already have led to insights into osteoporosis, the loss of bone calcium.

And the collision of contrasting traditions from the two sides of the old Iron Curtain is fascinating. At Houston I met Michael Foale, the space-walking Brit astronaut who famously took part in a Mir docking mission. He told me something of the culture clashes: for example a Houston mission planner turned up to prepare for the mission in Moscow with volumes of material, while his Russian counterpart turned up with a pencil.

But the Americans, though many would deny it, need the Russians.

The first American visitors were struck by how bad the Mir looks in space: meteorite holes all over, big solar-cell tiles crudely glued in place and badly degraded, and the interior was cluttered, with new equipment and replacement parts stuck down wherever there was room. The Russian programme *is* a lot more primitive, technically, than the US. But the Russians have learned how to keep a station in space for more than a decade, while Shuttle missions last no more than a couple of weeks. The Americans have still got to learn the skills of long-endurance space travel; perhaps that will be the key lesson of the ISS.

But can humans even survive in space?

Chapter 9

The Cruellest Sea

Oh, write not of me 'Died in bitter pains',
But 'emigrated to another star!'

— Helen Hunt Jackson

It is the year 2020. A near-Earth asteroid, a flying mountain of steel, is being approached by a mining craft from Earth. The asteroid's riches are expected to transform the planet's economy. The ship has been guided here by its pilot's navigational skills. As the craft gently nuzzles against coal-dark asteroid dust, the pilot signals success to her mission controllers on Earth.

The pilot is an astronaut who can navigate through space, manipulate her environment and control complex machinery. But she is not human. Her streamlined, torpedo-shaped body – about as long as your arm – is a rich burnt-orange, mottled black. Wing-like fins ripple elegantly alongside the body. The head is crowned by a beak surrounded by flipper-like arms, and there are two forward-looking eyes, blue-green rimmed with orange.

Alien eyes. Intelligent.

She is *Sepioteuthis sepioidea*: a Caribbean reef squid – or, rather, a genetically enhanced descendant of modern squid. Drifting in cool Earth water, the squid can feel the feather-touch of new gravity. Beneath the translucent skin of her habitat she can see a grainy, grey-black ground, a jagged horizon, barely tens of metres away.

She flashes her triumph, her mantle skin tingling. At last, with a sense of excitement, she slips her arms into the waldoes and prepares to begin the exploration of the asteroid . . .

This may seem a fantastic vision. But it may come to pass – for the human body simply isn't designed for space.

Space journeys are *long*. Even the Moon is three day's travel away. If we go further out we are considering sites that may be many years' journey away from Earth. After forty years of manned spaceflight we know a great deal about the deleterious effects of long-term space travel on human bodies.

It shouldn't really be a surprise. Your body is, after all, the result of four billion years of evolution that has taken place exclusively in a strong gravity field under a thick, moist blanket of air. So it takes a great deal of technological support for it to survive a long-duration spaceflight.

Most of a typical day in space, in fact, would be consumed with the chores of survival.

Your first task might be to swab the walls of your living quarters with disinfected wipes. Microgravity lowers your immunity response – because of a reduced number of lymphocytes in the blood – and besides, in space, micro-organisms tend to flourish, surviving on free-floating water droplets in the air. So, every couple of weeks, you have to wash down the walls.

After that, you will have to get through a lot of exercise to counteract the effects of microgravity: probably at least two hours of hard physical work-out every day, with a treadmill, or an exercise cycle, or bungee cords.

The human body can adapt to microgravity, after a fashion. The various functions of the body eventually, after a couple of months, settle down to a new equilibrium. The neurovestibular system, the balance mechanism within the ear, is the first to suffer – hence the space sickness that hit you in the first few days after launch – but also the first to recover. The body's fluid balance adjusts next, and then the cardiovascular system, the heart and blood vessels.

But the new equilibrium is not what your body is designed for. Your heart has less to do than usual, and so it is taking it easy, and is tending to shrink. And besides, as there is no gravity to pull blood down into your legs, your blood distribution is pretty confused, with too much fluid hanging around in your head. Your hind brain, which doesn't know about microgravity, thinks that is a symptom of too much fluid in your body, and is releasing a hormone telling your kidneys to release more urine. And that way lies dehydration. So you have to drink an extra five pints of fluid a day, laced with water–salt imbalance counteragents.

The Russians, veterans of long-duration spaceflight, have developed a number of ingenious gadgets to help – for example the penguin suit: elastic straps that try to pull you into a foetal position all the time, so your muscles are constantly working, as if against gravity. (The penguin suit is so called because it makes you waddle around on the ground during training.) And then there is the *chibis* (a Russian word for the lapwing), reinforced trousers that reduce the air pressure over the legs, to make the heart work harder to pull blood up from your lower body. Effective, but hardly comfortable.

You also have to submit, every two or three days of your mission, to electrocardiograms, seismocardiograms and measurements of your breathing rates and volume; and once a week you have to spend a whole day on a much more thorough checkout, which includes measurements of phases of cardiac contraction, heartbeat volume, venous pressure and vascular tone in different parts of the body, blood circulation in your head, lung ventilation, etc. All of this is fed back to the doctors on Earth. But it amounts to an awful lot of productive time lost out of every week.

Perhaps the most serious problem is the loss of calcium from your bones. Most of it gets washed away by all the extra urine you make. This could cause your bones to become brittle, or give you kidney stones, which is something you *really* don't want to happen so far from a qualified surgeon.

•

While exercise won't fix everything, it is important. But it is dull and uncomfortable; taking a shower is no great pleasure, since your eyes sting from the drifting soap for a full day afterwards, and it takes hours to towel the plastic shower stall dry before it can be folded up and put away.

Even going to the lavatory, notoriously, is an unpleasant adventure in space.

The Space Shuttle orbiter commode is a thing of steel and bolts and little metal labels, like something out of a military aircraft. There are thigh bars, cushioned and heavy, that swing across your legs to clamp your behind to the seat. Happily NASA has provided helpful instructions: *It is essential that a tight seal is maintained between the buttocks and the seat* . . . Hoses are provided to take urine to a tank, for storage or dumping in space; the funnels are colour-coded to ensure they aren't mixed up with your crewmates'.

Getting rid of your solid waste is actually easier. You start up the slinger, a spinning drum under the commode. Your waste sticks to the walls of the drum, and later you turn a switch to expose the drum to vacuum, and the waste is frozen and dried out. It seems crude, but is a rather better arrangement than what the Apollo crews once endured: an undignified business of plastic bags and wet-wipes, which included the necessity to *knead* the waste inside its bag to mix in antibacteria chemicals. Oh, the glamour!

Still, perhaps the problems of microgravity can be overcome. There have been experiments in using electromagnetic fields to stimulate bones and muscles in the absence of gravity. And more subtle solutions may be available. After all there are large mammals – for example, dolphins and whales – which live in the effectively weightless environments of the sea, without apparent problems of fluid distribution and bone calcium loss.

But if you are to survive in deep space, beyond the shield of Earth's magnetosphere and thick layer of atmosphere, your ship must protect you from a much more insidious hazard: radiation, high-energy particles and photons which can knock apart the atoms of your body.

Space is filled with an invisible sleet made up of three kinds of ionising radiation. There is a steady drizzle of *solar cosmic rays* – the regular solar wind, a proton-electron gas streaming away from the sun, boiled off by the million-degree temperatures of the corona – and *galactic cosmic radiation*, a diffuse flood of heavy, high-energy particles from remote stars, even other galaxies, which soak through the Solar System from all directions. And then there are SPEs, *solar particle events,* storms on the sun which cause intense doses of radiation. If you are caught in a solar storm you will have to retreat to your shelters, with their heavy plating of aluminium and water tanks clustered around the walls. To be caught out in the open is, bluntly, lethal.

Probably your spacecraft's hull will shield you from the worst of the effects of cosmic radiation. Still, if your mission lasts years, even if you avoid solar storms, your cumulative dose may amount to a few hundred rem – not lethal, but you have significantly increased the risks of cancer and leukaemia later in life. A single mission to Mars would take you above your advisory career radiation dosage: not an undertaking to be accepted lightly.

Humans are not, self-evidently, adapted to space travel.

Not only that, they are expensive.

It's hard to argue with the numbers. A Space Shuttle orbiter, in orbit, weighs around eighty-five thousand kilos. Of that only a third, typically, is payload. Most of the rest is plumbing, there to keep the humans alive, contributing nothing directly to a mission's goals. Humans are heavy, costly, soggy items to haul into space.

And humans, as heavy bags of water and bone, can get in the way: a sneeze at one end of the International Space Station may result in the wrecking of a delicate protein crystal growth experiment at the other.

But, to explore the Solar System and beyond, maybe it isn't necessary to send humans at all.

Speaking to the British Interplanetary Society in 1968, Sir Arthur C. Clarke said that when in 1945 he proposed twenty-four-hour-orbit communications satellites he imagined they would be large manned space stations (somebody would have to replace all those valves). But thanks to advances in electronic miniaturisation, even by the early 1960s, the first comsats were in fact about the size of beer barrels: no need for humans at all.

If anything this trend is accelerating. Our bravest space pioneers today are not humans, but robots.

For a long time a vicious circle operated in the development of robot spacecraft, making them grow in complexity, weight and cost. The first US satellite, Explorer 1, weighed less than five kilos. Cassini, launched in 1997 to study Saturn and its moons, weighed a massive five thousand five hundred kilos. Explorer cost six million dollars; Cassini cost four *billion*.

Of course we have achieved great things with the big, complex robot spacecraft of the past. Galileo reached Jupiter, releasing an atmosphere entry probe which should hit the planet in December. And in 2004 Cassini is due to place a lander on Titan, Saturn's mysterious moon.

But the great expense of such craft as Cassini means fewer spacecraft eating up the available funds: NASA launched a thousand spacecraft over the decade 1985–95, but only *eleven* of those left Earth orbit. With fewer missions there was a greater need to ensure success – more backup systems, more testing – all of which drove up costs still further. And when a mission did fail – like the Mars Observer, lost as it approached the planet in 1993 – a large hole was left in the overall programme.

Recently NASA has sought to break this cycle with a new 'better-faster-cheaper' approach: a new generation of simple spacecraft built with modern, lightweight components. The individual craft will be so cheap and plentiful that if any one probe fails (as more than one has) the programme hole will be comparatively small.

The low-cost approach was quickly proven. Clementine, launched in 1994, was America's first probe to the Moon since Apollo. Clementine was really a military technology test bed; but because the NASA lunar exploration of the 1960s concentrated on surveying landing sites for Apollo around the Moon's equator, Clementine could hardly help but make major discoveries. It found, for instance, the South Pole Aitken crater, the largest in the Solar System at two thousand five hundred kilometres wide – and all at a total cost of just eighty million dollars, compared to a hundred *billion* (at today's prices) for Apollo. This was followed by the Lunar Prospector, a highly successful spacecraft no larger than a dustbin.

Looking ahead, NASA has planned cut-price missions to Mars to cover every launch opportunity every two years. The Mars Pathfinder, launched in December 1996, was a direct-entry lander, the first probe to land on Mars since Viking in the 1970s. Despite embarrassing recent failures (it is possible to be too fast, too cheap) this is an exciting and optimistic programme.

And, as it becomes possible to make robots even smaller and smarter, NASA is making still more ambitious plans.

In the short term there will be *tiny* spaceships, smaller than toys, using microelectronic and micromechanical systems of telemetry, comms, data storage, guidance and payload control. Even the rocketry will be shrunk. NASA envisages a 'digital propulsion chip': a bank of solid rocket motors you could hold in the palm of your hand. The tiny motors can be addressed individually to get a high degree of manoeuvrability and control. Further out the miniaturisation may go further, perhaps all the way down to the nanotech scale.

And these tiny ships will get smarter. Autonomous control systems will be able to make their own decisions in regions so remote from Earth that ground control is impractical because of lightspeed delays.

The first applications will be modest. A larger craft might store a dozen throwaway miniaturised drones with lifetimes of, say, forty-eight hours, to carry out simple repairs and fly-around inspections.

Further out the potential for this technology is staggering. Even within the limitations of our current and foreseeable launch capabilities, microrobots will be able to reach the most remote and exciting places in the Solar System.

NASA is planning, for example, a probe to land on the icy surface of Europa, a moon of Jupiter. The probe will melt its way through the icy crust with lasers, and launch submarines into the liquid-water ocean which may exist beneath. A journey to Europa's surface is so fuel-expensive that the probe can be no larger than a toy, and yet it will be so far from Earth it will have to be smart enough to make its own on-the-spot decisions on how to proceed.

The only direct justification for the cost and risk of throwing humans into space has been our smartness and flexibility. When the robots are just as smart and flexible, who needs humans?

Ah, but what about the sense of wonder? We could identify with Armstrong on the Moon. Could we identify with a robot explorer of Mars or Europa or Pluto with not a trace of humanity about it? And why should we vote for their still-substantial price tag?

The story of NASA's Pathfinder to Mars might be a pointer to the future. Pathfinder was a lander with a small rover, capable of crawling to nearby rocks and performing simple tests. And NASA, seeking to build support for its programmes, encouraged us to anthropomorphise, asking us to support the plucky little robot as it struggled to survive a Martian night. NASA even reached the kids by licensing toy manufacturers to make replicas.

There was no need for a Neil Armstrong. The robot itself was the hero. We can imagine a future in which we humans are content to sit at home, happy and passive consumers and tax-payers, cheering on the gallant robots as they go where we no longer have the will to follow.

But maybe even robots aren't the ultimate answer.

Maybe if we are seeking to recruit space travellers we should, with new humility, look around at our fellow species. What of the cephalopod astronaut I sketched at the opening of this chapter?

Consider the facts.

Squid are extremely smart molluscs, functionally equivalent to fish. In fact they seem to have evolved – a long time ago, during the Jurassic – in competition with the fish. They are highly efficient predators. They have senses based on light, scent, taste, touch, sound (including infrasound), gravity, acceleration, perhaps even an electric sense.

Squid speak to each other.

Their hides sparkle with patterns made by sacs of pigment granules surrounded by muscles. A squid can control its skin patterns consciously, to make bands, bars, circles, annuli, dots. It can even animate the display. A given squid signal seems to be made up of a number of components: the skin patterns, skin texture – rough or smooth; posture – the attitude of the limbs, head, body, fins; and locomotor components – whether the squid is resting, jetting, hovering, grabbing, ink-jetting. There may be electric or sonic components too; we can't be sure.

Are the signals a true language? We've been able to isolate a number of primal linguistic components which combine in a primitive grammar. But we're not clear what they talk *about*. Squid live only a couple of years, mating once or twice. And a squid shoal is not a community like ours. They shoal for mutual protection, but they don't play or groom, and they hunt individually. It's not clear to us why such short-lived, only partially social animals need such complex communication systems. But they are there.

We're beginning to learn how squid function. We know that a squid's neural layout isn't like ours. A squid has two nerve cords running like rail tracks the length of her body, studded with pairs of ganglia, and the forward ganglia pair is expanded into a mass of lobes. But we believe we've identified the areas of the brain responsible for learning. (This was proven, unpleasantly, by cutting away parts of squid brains to see what happened.) We could surely use some comparatively simple genetic engineering to make squid smart – or, rather, smarter.

But *why* would we wish to enhance the squid? They could certainly perform useful work for us in the ocean – for example, working on sea farms. But is it possible they could operate outside the Earth altogether?

Eerily, it is almost as if the squid have been evolved for the conditions of space travel, as we self-evidently haven't.

Unlike us, squid live in free-fall anyhow. Their life-support requirements are simple: a bubble of water with a basic oceanic ecosystem. (The bubble, in fact, would be sufficient to shield squid astronauts from radiation hazards.) The squid can navigate, in three dimensions, with their powerful predators' eyes. They can communicate. And they can manipulate their environment.

If we made them just a little smarter, the squid would make fine astronauts . . .

But there is danger for us in this prospect.

The lethal ocean that separates our Earth from other worlds represents a stupendous challenge. But we can already envisage other creatures that may rise to that challenge, if we fail to meet it. If we launch these surrogate astronauts, perhaps at first we would imagine we could exert control over them. But surely that illusion would soon dissipate, as we cowered forever on the shores of our primaeval ocean, and *they* swam outwards into that harder, greater sea.

THREE

•

Sister Worlds

Chapter 10

Dry as Toast

We is here, man! We is here!

— Eugene A. Cernan, Apollo 17

Gerard K. O'Neill was perhaps the key space colony visionary of
the 1970s.

O'Neill, imagining cities in space, argued convincingly that the
limits to economic growth could be overcome by expansion into
space. However, O'Neill made the assumption that the space
programmes planned in his era would be achieved, and would
provide the capability to maintain the economic growth required by
civilisation, as projected at the time.

But those ambitious space programmes did not materialise.
Starting from today, we've lost thirty years' development compared
to O'Neill's space-colonisation timetable.

And meanwhile the human population has kept right on growing.

Not only that, there is a continuing growth in wealth per person.
Even a pessimistic extrapolation shows that we may need a total
economic growth of a factor of *sixty* over the twenty-first century if
we are to maintain such numbers.

Can we use the resources of space to maintain these ferocious
growth rates?

Modern updates of O'Neill's timetables are speculative, but the numbers they generate are startling. They indicate, for example, that if we aim to continue our current growth in energy consumption we need to be able to use power from space by, say, 2020.

By 2050 we will need a working economy in space, returning power, microgravity industrial products and scarce resources to the Earth. We might even be feeding the world from space by then. We'd surely need tens of thousands of people in space to achieve this, an infrastructure extending maybe as far as Jupiter. This is just *five decades* away.

By 2100 we probably need to aim for economic equivalence between Earth and space. It's impossible to hazard what size of economy this implies: some analysts believe we may need as many as a *billion* people living beyond the Earth by then.

These are expansionist dreams, and perhaps cannot, or even should not, be pursued, but note that these are simply projections from our *current rates of growth*; the only alternative is to reduce our expectations.

But even if we abandon growth, space resources may be a solution – the only solution – to Earth's difficulties over coming decades. If we simply lifted power-generating facilities, for instance, off the surface of the planet, we would drastically reduce the pressure we place on the planet's environment and carrying capacity.

And we might go further and seek out mines in the sky: to retrieve from other worlds raw materials which are difficult, expensive or even impossible to obtain on Earth, and thereby removing another major source of waste heat and pollution from the Earth.

But how are we to achieve all this?

The Apollo astronauts carried with them to the Moon every scrap of food and water and air they would need during their journey, but, because of these constraints, they were restricted to a stay of just three days. Humans have lived in space for a year or more on the Mir space station; but our space stations are not self-sufficient. Even the new International Space Station, while cleansing and recycling its air and water, will rely on food and other supplies brought up regularly from Earth.

This can't go on. When we consider mines in the sky, we are really talking about colonies, capable of sustaining people for months or years at a time.

If we are to live and work in space, we must seek out resources there; we must learn, one way or another, to live off the land. But where?

Perhaps we should begin by considering our first port of call beyond the Earth.

Take a fresh look at the Moon. You can tell a great deal about it just by studying it with your naked eye, from Earth.

Our nearest neighbour is a small, airless world. You can see there is no air because no atmosphere blurs the Moon's edge. The bright background areas you see are *terrae*: very ancient ground, highlands heavily worked by meteorite impacts. The *maria*, the darker patches – the features that make up the 'face' of the Man in the Moon – are pools of frozen lava. These formed a little later in the Moon's evolution, perhaps when impacts opened up wounds in the Moon's cooling surface, punctures through which runny lava flowed, pooling in the lowlands.

The Moon is literally covered by impact craters. Unlike Earth, the Moon was so small it lost its inner heat quickly, and its interior froze to stillness. The Moon's surface coalesced rapidly, and has since been shaped, not by Earth-like tectonic-plate geology, but by the impacts. The older craters tend to be larger. The Moon's surface is a frozen record of the savage but dwindling bombardment all the planets (including Earth) have suffered since their formation. Some of the impact craters are mighty indeed, like the Mare Imbrium, so big it's visible to your naked eye as the Man in the Moon's right eye.

Just by looking from Earth, you can even tell what the Moon's surface would be like to walk on.

If the Moon were a ball of bare rock, it would have a bright spot of light under the sun, a highlight like a bowling ball, making it look three-dimensional. But that isn't what we see: the Moon looks rather like a flat, mottled plate. This is because the Moon is covered in dust.

Since its formation the Moon's surface has been subject to an endless sandblasting by micrometeorites, tiny rock particles that drift between the planets. This endless erosion has pulverised the surface, covering it with a thick blanket of clinging dust. And the dust scatters the sunlight.

From the beginning of recorded history, humans have dreamed and speculated about life on the Moon.

The Greeks understood that the Moon is a world – a planet floating in space, like the Earth. They believed that the dark areas really were seas and the bright regions land. This belief has echoes today in the nomenclature of the Moon. The Greeks bequeathed us the language of *terrae* and *maria*. Plutarch, of the first century AD, even believed that the Moon was inhabited by people.

Serious interest in the Moon as an abode of life began with *Somnium* (1634) by Johannes Kepler. Kepler's influence on astronomy is well known. *Somnium* was a meditation on the then-new sun-centred theory of the Solar System: Kepler speculated on how the heavens would appear from the Moon, and on an ecology for the Moon.

Speculations on life on the Moon continued through the seventeenth and eighteenth centuries. As late as 1835 Richard Adams Locke was able to cause a sensation with his infamous 'Moon Hoax' in the *New York Sun*, purporting to describe the fantastic inhabitants of the Moon as observed by astronomer Sir John Herschel with a new southern hemisphere telescope.

But by the time lunar voyages began to become a matter of engineering rather than fantasy, the Moon had already been extensively explored telescopically, and the prospect of life, at least on the lunar surface, was beyond credibility. Jules Verne's circum-lunar travellers in *Around the Moon* (1870) observed only traces of life in deep craters on the far side of the satellite.

Still, lifeless or not, before the Apollo missions it was a given for space visionaries that the apparently barren Moon would harbour hidden riches for future human colonists.

As late as 1968, Arthur C. Clarke, in *The Promise of Space*, was able to list an optimistic catalogue of future lunar uses. Perhaps there were metallic ores which could 'pay for any lunar exploration programme a hundred times over'. The Moon could serve as an observation platform for X-ray astronomy. The scientific study of the Moon could revolutionise our understanding of the Solar System. And so on. Above all, the Moon could be colonised. In fact, 'the future of lunar and . . . Solar System . . . exploration . . . depends on our ability to find supplies of all kinds on the Moon'.

And, as Clarke noted, 'The most valuable substance of all – as it is on Earth, when in short supply – would be water.' Water would support life, and could be cracked into hydrogen and oxygen to supply rocket fuel. The Moon would become a filling station outside Earth's deep gravity field, much easier to land on and depart from, which could be used to fund a general expansion into the Solar System. '[Water] certainly exists on the Moon; the question is where, and in what form.'

Clarke was right to emphasise water's importance. We need a lot of ingredients to live, but water is by far the most fundamental; by comparison, carbon, hydrogen, nitrogen and other essential elements amount to only fractions of the mass of living tissue. It seems a fair bet that if we can find water, we can find a way to live (and as we consider further destinations in subsequent chapters, water will be regarded as a key goal).

And water on the Moon was a perfectly reasonable assumption for Clarke to make in 1968. There were lunar formations which seemed to indicate the presence of permafrost. Perhaps there was ice in underground caves. The physicist John Gilvarry went so far as to argue as late as 1960 that the lunar seas' dark colour might be due to sediment deposited in a deep lunar ocean. The water would have been a kilometre deep globally, even deeper in the *maria*, and the rings and shelves observed in the Moon's basins were marks of the retreat of this life-rich sea.

But Apollo brought a grave disappointment.

The analysis of the Moon rocks betrayed not the slightest trace of water, either now or in the past. The samples showed no ice, no water vapour trapped in bubbles in volcanic rocks, not even water bound chemically to the rocks, Clarke's most pessimistic assumption in 1968. The dark lunar seas proved to be made of basalt, not organic sea-bottom scum.

Not only that, the lack of water during the lunar crust's early melting periods ensured that big hydrothermal ore deposits – the type which produce much of Earth's mineral wealth – are completely absent from the Moon. The Moon seemed bone dry, and impoverished besides.

To many, even inside the space programme, Apollo, intended as a first step into the cosmos, in the end served only to prove that we *cannot* colonise space. The space visionaries and science fiction writers turned away from the Moon: once the stepping-stone to the Solar System, the Moon had turned out to be a useless ball of slag – and perhaps even worse than useless; Mars campaigner Robert Zubrin regards the Moon as a siren distraction on the road to better places.

As the Apollo results matured in analysis, however, a certain cautious optimism about the Moon began to emerge once more.

The Moon's only resource is rock. But, while the rocks contain no water, they are forty per cent oxygen by weight.

NASA engineers have already trialled technologies for baking air out of lunar rock. Imagine a cylinder two metres tall, with a hopper for ore at one end, and pipes for circulating hydrogen and water and dumping waste: a clunky-looking, robust piece of chemical engineering. The idea is that you blow hydrogen across heated regolith – crushed Moon rock. That extracts the oxygen from a Moon rock ore called ilmenite, an oxide of iron and titanium, to make water. This technology is mature, what the engineers called 'gaslight era' – that is, recognisable to a Victorian engineer – and the test beds are made of standard parts: swazelock fittings, copper gasket seals, steel tubing. Even the furnace is commercial, a nichrome-wound fuse design.

Other common and useful elements on the Moon are silicon, aluminium, calcium, iron, titanium and magnesium. From lunar rock you can make ceramics, concrete and glass. The absence of water is actually an advantage for the manufacture of glass, which can be made much tougher than on Earth: in the lunar cities of the future, it could serve as steel or concrete does in Earth cities.

As for power, the endless, unshielded sunlight is an obvious energy resource; perhaps areas of the wide, flat *mare* plains could be melted in place to form gigantic solar collectors.

Hydrogen and helium, too, may be present, implanted in the lunar soil by billions of years of solar wind. These light elements could be mined to make rocket fuel to burn with the oxygen, or even for export to Earth as a resource for fusion power stations. (Earth doesn't have much helium-3, the 'right kind' of the element for the most effective operation of fusion plants.)

This is not to say it will be easy.

The lunar conditions invalidate much of our terrestrial experience of heavy industry and manufacturing. The dust, shattered by meteorite rain but unweathered, is extraordinarily abrasive, damaging any seals you try to make (as the Apollo astronauts learned). The airlessness makes most lubricants useless and is liable to cause vacuum welds. There isn't even any convection for heat dissipation. And the low gravity causes problems with simple things like fluid flow (because of novel bubble effects in liquids).

The lack of water would also cause significant problems. Mining on Earth depends heavily on abundant water for cooling and lubrication, the movement and separation of materials, and the solution and precipitation of metals. There would also be problems with 'beneficiation', the treating of mined ore to produce a more uniform, upgraded mineral concentrate suitable for further treatment. The lack of water would rule out such methods as froth flotation and gravity concentration, though such methods as electrostatic concentration would be possible. Smelting and refining would also be dependent initially on the availability of imported reagents.

The Moon may not be the easiest place to colonise or mine. But it is a whole world waiting for us – as much land area as North America, and almost all of it is unexplored – a relatively easy three days' travel away, much closer than Mars or any other destination. We *know* we can get there.

And if we were, after all, to find water then the Moon could become the most important world in the Solar System.

Chapter 11

The Hidden Ocean

And Noah he often said to his wife when he sat down to
  dine,
'I don't care where the water goes if it doesn't get into
  the wine.'

— G. K. Chesterton

And the squirrels often say to us
' We don't care where the nuts go if
  not into the ground.'

The Apollo astronauts found a Moon 'as dry as toast', in Charlie
Duke's words. But there are many places on the Moon Apollo
never visited and, in some of them, water may yet be found.

At the lunar poles, far from Apollo's cautious equatorial landing sites,
there are deep craters, permanently shielded from sunlight. If water
reached the Moon – for instance, delivered there by comet impacts –
then perhaps it could have collected in those cold traps (individual
water molecules would 'hop' at random over the hot lunar surface
until they found shade, where they would remain indefinitely).
Perhaps there are great frozen lakes at the lunar poles, layered with
dust, just waiting for us to mine them.

A key objective of NASA's 1998 space probe Lunar Prospector was
to search for signatures of this hypothetical cold-trap water. Unfortunately, the evidence it returned was controversial and incon-
clusive. Even a brave final experiment, in which Prospector was
crashed into the Moon's surface in the hope of producing a plume of
vaporised water, failed to prove the hypothesis one way or the other.

The cold-trap theory already had its doubters. Models of comet impacts show they deposit little volatile material on the Moon anyhow, the rest being vaporised and blasted off the Moon's surface before it can be trapped. And even if any ice was caught in the shadows, it wouldn't be protected for ever. The Moon's axis is unstable, so that the Moon tips this way and that over a period of hundreds of millions of years. Those 'permanent' shadows aren't permanent after all; no cold trap could persist to bring ancient water to the present.

And besides, the Moon, for all its battered appearance, has actually suffered comparatively few major impacts in its recent history. The big lunar craters, including its giant impact basins, are mostly very ancient: the Moon has suffered no impact as severe as Earth's dinosaur killer, sixty-five million years ago, for three *billion* years. It is easy to understand why. Earth's deep gravity well tends to draw in most possible impactors, effectively shielding the Moon.

So, if our hope of finding water in cold traps is evaporating, are we back to the toast-dry Moon?

Not necessarily. But to understand why, we have to take a look at the formation of the Moon.

Earth, Moon and the other planets condensed, almost five billion years ago, from a swirling cloud of dust and gases. That primordial cloud was rich in volatiles – three per cent of it was water, for instance. We know that is so from studying the composition of asteroids and meteorites, which are left-over fragments of the cloud.

But there is an anomaly. If you add up all the water on Earth, in the oceans and atmosphere and the ice sheets, it totals to less than a *tenth* of that three per cent fraction. Where did the rest of the water go?

The prevailing wisdom is that most of Earth's water was lost during the great heat of Earth's formation, as it collapsed from a cloud of rock. Perhaps the water of our oceans was delivered *after* Earth's formation, by comet impacts.

But some scientists believe that much of that primordial water is still there within the Earth, perhaps four hundred kilometres down, deep in the mantle.

The water wouldn't be present as a series of immense buried oceans. Rather it would be scattered as droplets, some as small as a single molecule, trapped inside crystal lattices of the minerals that form under the intense pressure down there, materials with names like wadsleyite and hydrous-D. These special forms could trap water within their structure, essentially exploiting the high pressure to overcome the tendency of the rising temperature to bake the water out. It is all a question of exotic mineralogy and the physics of solids.

Nobody has dug into the Earth deep enough to prove this one way or the other – but there may be indirect evidence.

Geologists have found water in minerals dragged up from hundreds of kilometres down by 'kimberlites', iron-magnesium rocks that haul up high-pressure mineral specimens like diamonds. Earthquake waves travel slowly in some parts of the mantle, and such waves would be slowed down by the presence of water. Maybe even giant volcanic events called 'continental flood basalts', found in great outpourings in Brazil, Namibia and elsewhere, might be associated with deep-water caches.

Some estimates say there should be as much as *five times* as much water buried within the Earth as in all its oceans and atmosphere and ice caps – and what is true of Earth could be true of the Moon.

The Moon is mostly made of material like Earth's mantle. The Moon is smaller than the Earth, cooler and more rigid, so that the centre of the Moon is like the Earth's mantle layers a few hundred kilometres deep. And it is precisely at such depths, on Earth, that you find water-bearing minerals.

If even *one tenth of one per cent* of the Moon's mass is water, that would amount to about five per cent of all Earth's water. A hidden ocean indeed.

The strongest objection to the notion that the Moon might harbour deep water is the prevailing theory of the Moon's origin. It is believed that a Mars-sized proto-planet slammed into young Earth early in the

Solar System's formation. Mantle material was driven from the Earth into an orbiting cloud. The cloud then collapsed to form the Moon (which is why the Moon is made of mantle-like rock). The great heat of the impact, and perhaps the later collapse, would surely have baked out any volatiles, including water.

. . . Wouldn't it? Maybe the water, suspended in the cloud that condensed into the Moon, got trapped once more in its interior. Maybe the impact theory of the Moon's origin is wrong altogether. Nobody knows.

Remarkably, we can think of another entirely independent mechanism for the creation of giant deep-water reservoirs on the Moon. Our worlds coalesced from a hail of impacting 'planetesimals' – proto-planets. Even after the principal worlds had formed, the great bombardment continued. The giant objects which created such immense impact features as the Moon's South Pole Aitken basin might easily have buried water at depths of many kilometres. This secondary mechanism, while not delivering such quantities of water as hydrosilicate trapping, could still have formed significant reservoirs beneath the surface.

These are provocative ideas. We don't have any evidence for deep lunar water yet – or any proof to the contrary, come to that. It would be buried in the core, so far down it surely wouldn't contribute to surface processes. But the Moon has deep quakes like the Earth's, emanating from the base of the Moon's mantle. And it has suffered flood basalt episodes: the dark lunar seas, the *maria*, are lakes of congealed lava.

The truth is that nobody knows if there is deep water on the Moon or not. What is certainly true is that hidden caches of water on the Moon would be an immense prize, certainly worth searching for – and certainly worth funding such a search.

But if the lunar water exists at all, it might be buried hundreds of kilometres down, perhaps close to the core itself. How could we ever make use of it?

There have been studies on the challenges of lunar mining. But they have focused on the problems of *surface* mining: merely scooping up the already pulverised regolith and cracking it for water and minerals. Little consideration has been given to the greater challenges of *underground* lunar mining.

Some aspects of deep underground mining on the Moon will actually be easier than on Earth. The Moon's lower mass gives it lower internal pressures, and the rock a greater rigidity and stability.

Some of our standard mechanical drilling techniques (percussion and rotary) would work, though we would have to think hard about cooling and lubrication. Other drilling methods (thermal, hydraulic, sonic, chemical) are presumably ruled out by the absence of air. It may be that, confronted by the hard, fine-grained basaltic rocks of the lunar mantle, more advanced drilling techniques (such as the use of lasers, electric arcs, magnetic induction techniques or even nuclear techniques) would prove more appropriate.

Even beyond the challenges of the lunar environment, the extraction of minerals from extreme depths poses significant difficulties.

The deepest operating mine on Earth was the Western Deep Levels Mine at Carltonville, Transvaal, South Africa, reaching some four kilometres in July 1971. A deeper hole, a geologic exploratory borehole, was made by the Soviets at Zapolarny, on the Kola Peninsula of Arctic Russia. By 1983 this reached twelve kilometres; at such depths the temperature had exceeded two hundred degrees Celsius, and the static pressure had risen to perhaps five thousand atmospheres. But to reach the deep interior of the Moon means challenging temperatures and pressures an order of magnitude higher than this.

Such an ambitious project goes far beyond most post-Apollo studies on the colonisation and industrialisation of the Moon. It may be that deep-mining activities would be undertaken only by a reasonably mature lunar base in the medium to long term. But if significant water caches on the Moon could be shown to exist, our view of the role of our sister world in our future would be transformed. It would become again the pivot on which the colonisation of the Solar System might depend – and perhaps we could even make the Moon itself bloom.

Take another look at the Moon.

Now, the Moon is blue.

Even a slim crescent Moon is much brighter than the full Moon of the past. And the crescent's edge is softly blurred by a band of light, which stretches part way around the dark half of the satellite. The band is the Moon's atmosphere. There is a thick band of what looks like cloud, piled up over the Moon's equator.

Sparks, perhaps ships, crawl over the globe. There are more lights, strung out in lines, on the darkened surface itself: towns or cities, outlining hidden continents.

And in the centre of the half-darkened hemisphere which faces you is a dazzling point glow. You know what that must be. The point source is the light of Earth, reflected from the oceans of the Moon . . .

Could it ever be possible?

Terraforming – making a world into a clone of Earth – is usually associated, in modern thinking, with Mars. Terraforming the Moon would be an even greater challenge.

The Moon is deficient in almost all the volatiles required for terrestrial life – carbon dioxide, nitrogen, water – and, unless they can after all be mined from the Moon, these would have to be imported, for example from a comet or an ice moon. Even then the Moon's month-long 'day' would cause problems; the new lunar atmosphere would freeze during the long nights (as in H. G. Wells's 1901 novel, *First Men in the Moon*). Perhaps some remedy like spaceborne mirrors, or even, in the long term, spinning up the Moon, could be deployed.

There are other problems. The Moon's low gravity would cause any new atmosphere to leak away (if slowly). Drainage would be a more immediate snag. Simply flooding the Moon's primordial land-scape would not be sufficient; without natural drainage channels, after the first rains the waters would tend to become trapped in the highland craters. And the lack of any geological activity would mean that in the very long run the Moon could not recycle its store of volatiles, as Earth does.

But still, if we plan the occupancy of the Moon over a very long period – thousands of years – then perhaps terraforming is the only solution. What if civilisation falls? What if our children forget how to maintain the machinery that keeps them alive? Only a *world* – stable, with deep biological reservoirs of water and carbon and air – is going to be big enough to sustain human life over millennia, or longer.

And there can be no doubt how beautiful it would be to stand on the Earth of the fourth or fifth or sixth millennium, and gaze up at a blue transformed Moon, no longer a neglected orphan, but a true sister planet . . .

But perhaps it is wrong to dream such dreams of reconstruction. Maybe we should accept the Moon for what it is.

Our disappointment with the Moon we found in the 1960s, compared to the rich world we had been led to expect, has coloured our view of it since. The Apollo 8 astronauts orbited the Moon in 1968. Homesick for their Christmas hearths, lacking the training to understand what they were seeing, the astronauts described the Moon by contrast with 'the good Earth' as a 'misshapen golf ball . . . a battlefield . . . a volleyball game played on a dirty beach . . .'

But the Moon has its own subtle beauty, as some of the astronauts appreciated. The Moon is an ancient world, heavily eroded, not by wind or rain, but by micrometeorite bombardment. Rising over its gentle slopes, the Earth is a bright blue, but when the sun is up the stars are invisible to human eyes, because of solar dazzle. To Neil Armstrong, looking out of his Lunar Module, the Moon actually seemed a friendly place, something like a beach; others were reminded of ski-slopes and sand dunes.

Perhaps it is time to outgrow our disappointment at the Moon, to open our hearts to the real Moon, and let it shape us, even as we shape it.

And, in an unexpected way, even if it lacks water, the Moon may be, after all, the stepping-stone to the future.

Earth, with its rich geology and complex biosphere, is probably unique. But we can expect to find small rocky worlds like the Moon everywhere, throughout the Galaxy, and beyond.

If we can live off the land on the Moon, we can live *anywhere*.

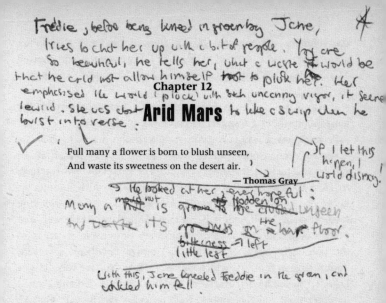

Chapter 12

Arid Mars

> Full many a flower is born to blush unseen,
> And waste its sweetness on the desert air.
>
> — Thomas Gray

It is not travel to the Moon of which we have dreamed over the centuries, but of journeys to a much more alluring sister world. To many people, the future of mankind beyond Earth means, simply, Mars. From Earth, you can see the surface of Mars: the only world other than the dead Moon of which this is true, the secret of its fascination for us.

But seen through a telescope Mars is blurred, elusive, tantalising. Until the first space probes, Mars served as a blank screen on which successive generations projected their dreams.

Galileo observed Mars through his early, crude telescope in 1610, but saw little more than its phases. The first useful drawing of Mars was made by Christiaan Huygens, in 1659; he mapped the area we now call Syrtis Major. In 1666 Giovanni Cassini spotted white polar caps. In 1837 Wilhelm Beer and Johann von Madler spotted a 'wave of darkening', a seasonal variation of albedo near the north polar cap.

The two moons of Mars were discovered by Asaph Hall in 1877.

And Secchi, in the 1860s, and Schiaparelli, in 1877, observed – in the moments of apparent clarity allowed by Earth's turbulent atmosphere – what seemed to be linear features on the tiny, blurred Martian disc. Schiaparelli called these lines 'channels' – in Italian, 'canali' . . .

The time was ripe, with these partial and dubious observations, for a most fantastic and wonderful hypothesis to be drawn.

Percival Lowell was a good American astronomer who ingeniously observed, among other things, dust storms in the Martian atmosphere. But he let Schiaparelli's language of 'canali' overwhelm him. In 1895 Lowell published a book called *Mars* in which he spun an image of a cool, arid, dying world of great red deserts and shrinking tracts of arable land. An intelligent race of Martians, said Lowell, had unified politically to build irrigation canals to transport water from the poles. This great civilisation had mown down any awkward 'mountains' in the way, which was why Mars's surface was flat – as Lowell believed he had observed. And that 'wave of darkening' must be vegetation, which bloomed across the dusty plains every Martian spring.

While Lowell's Barsoom-like Mars gripped the public imagination, astronomers made slow but steady progress in unveiling the Mars of science.

At the time telescopic photography didn't reveal as clear an image as was possible with the naked eye, so drawings remained the best source of images of Mars. These were subject to error and subjective interpretation. Still, the best astronomers noted that the 'linear' features would resolve themselves into disconnected dots and patches in the moments of highest clarity. It began to look as if Lowell had been mentally 'constructing' his canals in a join-the-dots fashion. Schiaparelli himself denied the existence of Lowell's 'canals'. And besides, the huge nets of straight lines Lowell saw didn't make sense when projected against a globe.

The atmosphere and surface of Mars were studied (from Earth) with thermocouples and spectrometers. Soon it emerged that Mars was too cold to sustain liquid water; and besides, it looked as if the polar caps were made of carbon dioxide ice, not water. There was so little water on Mars that Lowell's grandiose network of canals could have no purpose.

Barsoom slowly crumbled, and in the early decades of the twentieth century a new paradigm of Mars emerged.

On the new arid Mars, there were no canals, no gorgeous Martian cities. But Mars was still a home away from home: basically Earthlike, with an atmospheric pressure maybe a tenth of Earth's. There was some water, and probably Mars held life, but it would be rather feeble: dour, unthreatening stuff, perhaps plants with tough, leathery skin to retain water. Humans living on Mars would evolve long legs, and huge lungs to strain at the mountain-top air.

As the most likely abode of extraterrestrial life, Mars was still seen as the first great stepping-stone en route to the stars, and an infinite future for humankind.

And serious engineers began to draw up plans to carry humans to Mars's red deserts.

The German engineer Wernher von Braun, who built Apollo's Saturn boosters, devised elaborate schemes to reach Mars, using the emerging technologies of his time. In 1953, in *The Mars Project*, von Braun proposed a mission on a heroic scale, with ten four-thousand-tonne spacecraft, each carrying seven men. The astronauts would have glided down to the surface in shuttles buoyed up by the thick atmosphere. By 1956 this vision had been scaled down to two ships each weighing a mere hundred and sixty tonnes.

The Apollo Moon programme was seen by NASA insiders as a stepping-stone to the ultimate goal, Mars. From the beginning von Braun had argued for the building of the Nova, a booster even bigger than the Saturn V that would have been capable of launching Mars missions, but he was overruled.

In 1962, after the Apollo-Saturn Moon flight system had crystallised, the engineers started to ask what else could be done with the technology to progress to the ultimate goal. They came up with EMPIRE, Early Manned Planetary-Interplanetary Roundtrip Expeditions. A Mars flyby option would have used a couple of Saturn V third stages, ganged together in Earth orbit and fired off on a minimum-energy trajectory to loop around Mars. It would have taken two or three Saturn V launchers, a seven-hundred-day round trip, all to deliver about one day of useful work at Mars: passing by at interplanetary speeds – *on the dark side*! But in the heady days of 1962, the point was *to go*, just like Apollo, rather than to achieve scientific goals.

Then, in 1964, the first successful Mars space probe, Mariner 4, made a close fly-by of the planet and gave the astronomers a profound shock. In the words of the US Information Service's booklet on the Mariner 4 mission, 'Where astronomers had expected to find features similar to those on Earth, Mariner 4's pictures clearly showed a terrain resembling that of the Moon. Huge craters pocked the surface . . .' *Craters*: despite the fact that Mariner 4 had been directed over an area where, even in 1964, canals had been expected.

A million dreams died with a single, grainy snapshot.

Things only got worse as more probes followed Mariner. The 'wave of darkening' was nothing to do with vegetation, but clouds and evaporation around the polar caps. And the air of Mars, which had been thought to be equivalent to Earth's at an altitude of maybe twice the height of Everest, was actually more like that at the edge of space.

In the 1970s the Viking landers carried experiments to look for Earth-like life. They found some odd chemistry, but the soil appeared to be not just dead but actually sterilised – blasted free of organic molecules, presumably through the action of the sun's ultraviolet light.

No flowers blushed unseen in the desert air of Mars: it was a shattering disappointment. But still the engineers continued to plan for Mars missions.

In 1969, as we have seen, NASA put forward strong plans for Mars missions, but received no approval. In the 1980s, Western analysts suspected the Soviets were building incrementally to a manned Mars (or, more probably to its moon, Phobos) mission, using Mir modules as the basis of an interplanetary craft. Cosmonauts had orbited Earth in their Salyut and Mir space stations for times comparable to a Mars flight. And the unmanned Phobos orbiter, in 1988, looked like a precursor to a manned mission.

But Soviet technology was always technically suspect. The Phobos probe failed, and the Soviet Union fell apart.

America looked to Mars again in 1986, following the *Challenger* Space Shuttle disaster. There was a brief mood of moral obligation to honour the lost astronauts by proceeding to new goals in space. In 1989 President Bush established the Space Exploration Initiative, planning to reach Mars by 2010, all at a cost, as estimated by NASA, of a whopping five hundred billion dollars over two decades. But there was no sustained political will, and the Initiative was quickly starved of funds by Congress.

Since then visionary planners have come up with a variety of ways to reach Mars with post-Space Shuttle technology. According to Robert Zubrin's 'Mars Direct' proposal, Mars would be reached with a wave of spacecraft capable of manufacturing return fuel from Mars's carbon dioxide atmosphere – a limited way to 'live off the land' and at a fraction of the cost of NASA's proposals.

One of the most intriguing, and fuel-efficient, ways to reach Mars was devised by Apollo 11 astronaut Buzz Aldrin in the 1980s. In Aldrin's plans a 'cycler' spacecraft would ferry endlessly between Mars and Earth on a twenty-six-month round trip, transferring crews and cargo. The feasibility of Aldrin's ideas needs to be proved, particularly refuelling at Mars. But if it works, the cyclers could be the stepping-stones to cheap Mars flights.

But what kind of world would these dogged travellers find?

The surface of Mars looks like the Arizona desert. But it is much more hostile.

Mars is smaller than the Earth, so gravity is only about a third of Earth's. It is further from the sun, so it receives considerably less solar energy. Its air is mostly carbon dioxide: very thin, and with a pressure about half of one per cent of Earth's. And because of the thin air, temperatures swing from eighty degrees Fahrenheit at noon to maybe two hundred below at night.

If you were to walk out unprotected on the surface of Mars, the planet would kill you rapidly: from freezing, exposure to the near-vacuum, and the unshielded ultraviolet rays of the sun. Mars, still the most hospitable place we know of beyond Earth, is lethal.

But if you could cross a hundred thousand years, you might find a remarkably changed Mars.

Mars is no longer red, but green and blue.

Mars has a green southern hemisphere, and a huge blue ocean covers the whole of the northern hemisphere, half the world. You can see the wakes of ships in the seas of Mars, and the lights of cities all over the night side. But some elements of the old red Mars have survived: you can see the huge volcanoes, like Olympus Mons, so big they stick up out of the thick, warm atmosphere. Their summits have been glassed over, to conserve some of the old red sands . . .

Could this happen? It would certainly be a monumental effort; vast amounts of energy and materials have to be added to Mars – or drawn from deep stores – to build a breathable atmosphere.

The key to the rebuilding of Mars may be carbon dioxide, well known as a greenhouse gas on Earth, capable of trapping the sun's heat. Mars's atmosphere is mostly carbon dioxide, but it is too thin for effective warming. But Mars does have a reservoir of additional carbon dioxide frozen at its polar caps.

First, the terraformers might melt the poles with giant orbiting mirrors, and spread black soot over the ice. And then they would inject other greenhouse gases into Mars's atmosphere: notably chlorofluorocarbon (CFC) gases, manufactured from raw materials in the Martian soil. CFCs have become recognised as a hazard on our overheating Earth; on Mars they may be the key to the future.

The key ingredient for life is water. Once again, Mars may have the resources required, waiting for us to tap. Viking and other probes showed evidence of water in the past: for example, what appear to be the remnants of gigantic, catastrophic flooding episodes, and perhaps even the tide marks of ancient seas. Mars may once have been warm and wet – indeed, the notorious Mars meteorites, which may or may not contain evidence of ancient life on Mars, certainly show traces of running water deep in Mars's past.

But if so, where did all the water go? Perhaps it was drawn into Mars's interior by geological processes like the great subduction flows on Earth. Mars, smaller than Earth, cooled more rapidly, making its crust and mantle more able to trap and store the water.

Some visionaries dream of immense underground aquifers, reservoirs trapped by caps of ice and permafrost, just waiting to be cracked. The vision of drilling a judicious mine and seeing that ancient water come gushing out of the ground is wonderful – but perhaps too wonderful; if the water were that easy to mine, surely random meteorite impacts would have cracked the permafrost 'lids' long ago. And if the water is held in deeper, more stable stores, it may take some time for the new warmth of Mars to diffuse into the deep layers of soil and rock, melting it and making it accessible.

But still, some dreamers imagine Mars transformed using a scheme like that sketched above, with a thick warm atmosphere in a hundred years, and a fully formed ocean in six hundred years: a long time, but comparable to great human technical projects like the Industrial Revolution.

Such a Mars, warm and wet, would be something like primitive Earth. Plants could flourish and there could be extensive agriculture. But humans could not breathe the carbon dioxide air; they could walk the surface without pressure suits, but would need to carry oxygen with them. And of course we would not be satisfied with such a half-finished job.

On Earth, microscopic plants laboured for billions of years to crack carbon dioxide and produce our oxygen-rich atmosphere. This process could be speeded up on Mars, but still, seen as an engineering process, the efficiency of producing oxygen in this fashion is very low. It might take ten to a hundred thousand years even for genetically enhanced plants to produce a breathable atmosphere.

And we humans need more than oxygen to survive. High concentrations of carbon dioxide are lethal to humans and animals;

our air is 'buffered' by large volumes of nitrogen, which also plays a key role in life processes.

There is nitrogen in Mars's atmosphere, but only enough for a thin scraping of life. It may be that more nitrogen is available in the form of compounds in the rocks. Alternatively nitrogen could be imported, from a comet or an ice moon, but the volumes and masses involved are stupendous. The availability of nitrogen on Mars is currently the key unknown in determining if Mars could be made into a home for life.

Some extravagant thinkers dream of much more dramatic solutions to the challenges of terraforming: for example, by crashing a moon of Jupiter into Mars's surface, or by using some technology barely imaginable to us, such as nanotechnology.

Still, in principle at least, we believe it could be done. And it would be a marvellous triumph for humanity when at last the day came when a human was able to walk out of a dome of Martian glass, remove her face mask, and take a deep lungful of the thin, clean, frosty air . . .

So some would argue, anyhow. Not everyone agrees. Even if we could terraform Mars – or the Moon, or other worlds – *should* we?

Proponents of terraforming would say that a living world is always better than a dead world: that to give life is the greatest gift humans could bestow. But right now we don't know if Mars has its *own* life or not; it would be nice to think we will check before wiping out any traces of it for ever.

And even if Mars is lifeless, what right do we have to rip it up and overlay it with a pale copy of Earth?

Even if you take the view that the worlds of the Solar System are put there for human exploitation, we must wonder whether it is wise to do it all so quickly. There is the question of good husbandry. The primaeval worlds, once gone, are gone for all time; if Mars is built over in a few centuries, or even a few millennia, it is hard to believe there will be time even to study what is being destroyed – and to determine what the potential of Mars might be in the future, if left alone.

And there are certainly more ways to treat a landscape than to pave it over.

In 1999 I visited Australia's Ayers Rock, known as 'Uluru' to the local Aboriginal population. It is a vast lump of hard, ancient sandstone, extensively carved by megayears of water flows, protruding uncompromisingly from the flat, arid land.

The Aborigines are not like Western people. Although they, like every other human population, have changed their world, still they touch the land lightly. To them, Uluru and neighbouring formations seem to have been as striking as a cathedral looming over mediaeval fields. And so the Aborigines made these rocks places of totemic and religious significance, spinning Dreamtime stories from cracks and folds, until the rocks became a kind of mythic cinema. It is a triumph of the imagination.

The great science fiction writer Brian Aldiss has argued that we should think of Mars as an Ayers Rock in the sky. Perhaps he is right.

Mars, after all, is more than a blank screen for our dreams. Mars is a small, strange world, very unlike the Earth, but it has a grandeur and appeal of its own. On Mars, there are volcanic mountains so tall they stick out of the atmosphere. On Mars, there *are* canals – not artificial, but a canyon system which stretches around half the planet, so long that it can be night in one part and daylight in another, causing great winds to roar along its length.

Mars – and the other worlds – have more to offer us than crude physical resources; they are resources for the spirit as well. Maybe a wiser strategy for our future would be 'pantropy': rebuilding mankind, not worlds; adjusting ourselves to meet the universe halfway. That way we could reach out to the real Mars, more inaccessible and difficult to colonise than we have dreamed in the past, and yet more strange and wonderful, perhaps beyond our imaginations.

And we may learn a lesson for the far future, for ultimately there will be *no* worlds like Earth, anywhere in the universe, whether we remark them or not.

Chapter 13

Children of the Sun

✓

She is Venus when she smiles.

— Ben Jonson

Bob (You are Mars Venus when you smile)
to Jane

We have looked, largely in vain, for the water of life on our nearest companion, the Moon, and the traditional repository of our dreams, Mars. Now we must look further into the Solar System.

Two worlds move within Earth's orbit, circling closer to the sun: Mercury and Venus. Will they play a role in our future?

If you could visit Mercury, you might imagine you had travelled to the Moon by mistake. It is a bony crescent against the black, even from a great distance clearly pocked by craters. But the sun is three times as large as seen from Earth or Moon, a bloated monster.

You skim over a pale, thickly cratered surface. There is only the barest shred of atmosphere, and so the craters and ridges and mountains and plains are picked out with a ruthless clarity, the exposed land shining bright, the shadows impossibly black. It is an antique, unmodified landscape, shaped in the violence of the Solar System's birth and baked by that too-close sun.

But there are no darker areas here, no equivalent of the Moon's great *maria*, the frozen seas of lava. And there are features unlike anything on the Moon: zones of crumpling, ridges and folds and cracks, like the wrinkled skin of a dried tomato, as if the planet shrank after its formation.

. The stand-out feature on Mercury is one immense impact structure, some thirty degrees above the equator. This is called Caloris Planitia. It is bounded by a ragged ring of mountains, with the tallest innermost, and lower foothills further out. Inside the ring there is a relatively smooth floor, marked by ridges, folds and rifts that follow roughly concentric patterns, like the glaze on an old dinner plate.

Once, some immense object punched into Mercury's crust, sending up huge rocky waves that gushed over hundreds of kilometres and then froze in place, for all time. Then molten rock from the mantle beneath pulsed up through the cracked ground, flooding the giant new basin, cracking and settling as it froze. The impact was clearly long ago; this monstrous scar is overlaid by many younger craters, dwindling in size the younger and fresher they are. Caloris is a coherent structure that spans some one-twelfth of the planet's circumference, a circle big enough neatly to encompass the Great Lakes.

On the far side of the planet is a very strange landscape: broken up, chaotic, almost shattered. This chaotic terrain is at the exact antipode of giant Caloris, the target of converging shock waves that travelled around the world. Rock-smashing energies must have focused here, and, some nine thousand kilometres from ground zero, made the land flex and crumble and boil.

Walking on Mercury's surface would be like walking on the Moon: the same undulating surface, heavily eroded, crater on crater, so the surface is like a sea of dusty waves. But if anything the erosion here is more complete. Any hills are stoop-shouldered, coated in regolith. The larger craters are little more than palimpsests, their features worn away.

But, unlike the Moon, this wearing away has not been caused by micrometeorite impacts but by thermal stress. Mercury's 'day', a combination of its orbit and slow rotation, lasts nearly six months. At noon, it gets hot enough to melt lead; in the night it is cold enough to liquefy oxygen. You are unlikely to see a rock crack open, however; everything that was going to shatter did so long ago.

What might strike you most strongly, however, is Mercury's gravity, which is about twice as strong as the Moon's – surprising for such a small world. Mercury is unusually massive because it is remarkably dense: closer to the density of pure iron, in fact, than to the rock of Earth's surface. It may be that Mercury was shaped by a primordial collision like the one that shaped proto-Earth, but in this case the collision stripped away the relatively light mantle rocks, leaving only a heavy iron core.

Mercury may one day have its uses: as an iron mine, for example, or as the site of the ultimate solar-power collector. And if we ever dare to engineer the sun itself, the iron-rich rocks of Mercury will surely be an essential resource.

But that is for a more distant future. For now, Mercury's origin, and that steady baking by the sun, have surely left it devoid of the water we need to survive.

So we move outward from the sun, to the world once considered Earth's true sister planet.

Venus is a world a little smaller than Earth, but swathed in a great monstrous ocean of atmosphere, almost all of it carbon dioxide: a hot bright layer that utterly blankets the ground from our view, so thick that at its base it exerts a pressure equivalent to a depth of a kilometre under Earth's oceans.

We do see some details in the upper atmosphere: shadowy forms, alternating bands of faint light and dark, hazy arcs. Near the equator there are sometimes yellowish spots, a little darker than the background. But these are nothing to do with any ground features. The hidden world within rotates slowly, completing a turn only after a startling 243 Earth days. But winds in the upper air, driven by the blowtorch heat of the sun working on this slow-spinning planet, roar fast enough to circle the planet in a few (Earth) days. All of those upper-air wisps and cloudy ghosts are artefacts of the strange, complex structure of Venus's great cloud decks.

Imagine penetrating those clouds.

Everywhere you look the world is murky red, both sky and land. This dense air, still, windless, is more like a deep ocean than our atmosphere. The sky above is like an overcast Earth sky, the light a sombre red, like a deep sunset, brighter than you expected, perhaps, but more Mars-like than Earth-like. The sun itself is invisible save for an ill-defined glare low on the horizon. The 'day' here lasts more than a hundred Earth days, a stately combination of Venus's orbit around the sun and its long rotation time – a day longer than Venus's year, in fact.

This is a world of volcanism.

You see continents separated by vast plains of flood basalts – frozen lakes of lava, like the *maria* of the Moon – and punctured by thousands of small volcanoes, shield-shaped, built up by repeated outpourings of lava. But there are giant shield structures, like Hawaiian volcanoes, that tower kilometres above the plains, covered in repeated lava flows.

And there are features which have no counterparts on Earth. There are 'pancake domes', steep-sided, flat-topped structures formed by sticky lava welling up through flaws in the crust. There are 'ticks', volcanoes with their flanks gouged away by huge landslides leaving ridges like protruding insect legs. There are 'arachnoids', domes surrounded by spider-web patterns of fractures and ridges. There are 'anemonae', volcanoes with flows that look like petals, pushing out across the plains.

And, most spectacular, there are 'coronae': utterly unearthly, rings of ridges and fractures. Some of these are thousands of kilometres across, giant features each big enough to straddle much of the continental United States. Perhaps they were formed by blobs of upwelling magma that pushed up the crust and then spread out, allowing the centre to implode, like a failed cake. There is much about this tortured world we do not yet understand.

There are even river valleys here: kilometres wide and thousands of kilometres in length, unlikely Amazons complete with flood plains, deltas, meanders and bars. One of these, called Baltis Vallis, is longer than the Nile, and probably the longest river valley in the Solar System. But it is very improbable that water was involved in the valleys' formation; perhaps they were cut by an exotic form of lava formed by a salty carbon-rich rock called carbonatite, that might have flowed in Venus's still hotter past.

You might be surprised to see craters on Venus, given that thick blanket of air. But they are everywhere, hundreds of them, spread evenly over the whole of the planet's surface. There is little erosion here; the air at the bottom of this turgid ocean of gas is very still, and so the craters have remained as fresh as when they were formed.

Few craters are small, for that thick air screens out the smaller impactors, destroying them before they reach the ground. To a large enough impactor even Venus's air (or Earth's oceans, come to that) is irrelevant as an obstacle. But, conversely, few of the craters are *large*. Certainly none of them compare with the giant basins of the Moon.

But those immense lunar basins date back to the earliest days of the Solar System, when the sky was still full of giant rogue planetesimals. And so we can tell that these Venusian craters are all *young* – no crater is much older than eight hundred million years.

That might seem an immense age, but the planets are five times older still. Eight hundred million years ago, something happened to Venus – something that distorted the entire surface, wiping it clean of older features, perhaps destroying four billion years of geological heritage.

As we come to understand the dark secrets of Venus's past, we are coming to understand the processes that shape it even today.

The geologists believe that when Venus was formed, it was almost a twin of Earth. If the water for Earth's final oceans was delivered by comet impacts, Venus should have been similarly blessed: thus Venus must once have had oceans of liquid water.

Of course Venus is closer to the sun, and even wet Venus was not an identical twin of Earth. Even then the air was dominated by carbon dioxide. The oceans were hot – perhaps as hot as two hundred degrees – and the atmosphere humid, laden with clouds. But, thanks to the water, plate tectonics operated, and much of the carbon dioxide was kept locked up in rocks which were periodically subducted into the mantle, just as on Earth.

Young Venus was a moist greenhouse, where life might have flourished.

But Venus, fatally, was just a little too close to the sun, and the climate, over the longest of timescales, was unstable.

Venus got hotter. There must have been a paucity of rain, a terrible drought . . . And, finally, the oceans themselves started to evaporate, extinguishing any life there might have been.

When all the oceans were gone, the water in the air started to drift to the top of the atmosphere. There it was broken up into hydrogen and oxygen by sunlight. The hydrogen escaped into space, and in the clouds the oxygen and remnant water turned to sulphuric acid.

After that, things got rapidly worse. When all the water was gone, plate tectonics halted. The shifting continents seized up, like an engine run out of oil. The planet's interior heat was trapped and built up, until it was released catastrophically.

Mass volcanism erupted. There were immense lava floods, giant new volcanoes. Much of the surface fractured, crumpled, melted – and the carbon dioxide locked up in the rocks began to pump into the atmosphere, thickening it further.

The surface cooled and solidified, but once again the inner heat was trapped, with none of Earth's relief mechanisms of plate tectonics. And eventually a day came when the land melted again . . . and again and again, each catastrophic episode resurfacing much of the planet and wiping away any older structures, such as ancient impact craters.

And that's why Venus's surface looks so young.

It would take very advanced colonists to find a way to live here.

Regarding water, the most optimistic possibility for both Venus and Mercury is the water trapped by the mechanisms we considered for the Moon: primordial water trapped in hydrosilicate rocks deep in the planets' interior, or perhaps buried there by giant impacts during the final stages of the worlds' formation, too deep for subsequent events to have baked it out. But even if it exists, the retrieval of deep-trapped water in the very hostile conditions of Venus or Mercury would be a monumental undertaking, and surely centuries away . . .

You sail into Venusian night. But there is no relief from the searing warmth, so effectively does the great blanket of air redistribute the heat; at midnight the air is only a few degrees cooler than at noon. And, as your eyes fully adapt to the dark, you see that there is still light here – but no starlight could penetrate the immense column of air above. *The ground itself* is shining: wrinkles and ridges and volcanic cones loom eerily from the dark.

On Venus, even at night, the rock is so hot it glows. This is no place for mankind.

Yet there is one place left in the inner Solar System where we might yet seek out water – unremarkable, unspectacular, and yet perhaps the richest lode of all.

Chapter 14

Sky Diamonds

Twinkle, twinkle, little star,
How I wonder what you are,
Up above the world so high,
Like a diamond in the sky.

— Jane Taylor

Blinkered, blinkered, little hole,
How I see you black as night
Out beyond the stars so bright
On an Earth-bound deadly roll.

On the very first day of the nineteenth century, a new world was discovered. It was an asteroid, now called Ceres – the first discovered, and the largest of them all, as it turned out – circling in the great waste between Mars and Jupiter.

Other asteroids soon followed: more than four hundred lumps of rock and ice by the end of that century. The asteroids are thought to be relics of the Solar System's formation, remnant planetesimals never gathered up into planets. And all those discovered at first were circling, in a more-or-less orderly fashion, in what has become known as the 'main belt' of asteroids.

But in 1898 a new type of asteroid was discovered. Christened Eros, this flying mountain can wander within the orbit of Mars – and even comes distressingly close to Earth.

Today we know of more than two hundred asteroids whose paths take them near our planet. They are known as near-Earth asteroids (NEAs). Some of them cross Earth's orbit or even circle within it. Most of them are only a few kilometres across or less, and take one to a few years to orbit the sun. Like their main belt cousins, the NEAs come in a variety of types. Some of them are mainly metal. Many are rocky. And some are rich in organic matter, apparently left over from the formation of the Solar System.

We believe the NEAs come from the main belt, perturbed by Jupiter's gravity and sent hurtling in towards Earth. Many of the NEAs show evidence of a violent origin, much shaped by impact. Some of them appear to be 'binary objects': two flying mountains bumping gently against each other, locked by gravity, perhaps remnants of a larger object shattered by immense collision.

Nobody pretends that we have found and tracked all the NEAs. There may be as many as two thousand more than a kilometre across, and maybe two *hundred* thousand more than a hundred metres across.

And about a fifth of them will eventually impact Earth.

'Eventually', in this astronomical context, encompasses billions of years. But future collisions are inevitable, and pose a threat to the long-term habitability of our planet.

The Chicxulub impact sixty-five million years ago, which probably caused the extinction of the dinosaurs, was sufficient to cause mass death, and to alter – drastically, and for all time – the evolution of life on Earth. But it was caused by an impactor no more than ten kilometres across. There are many NEAs of that size, and many much larger.

If we saw a NEA coming sufficiently far away, we could perhaps push it away with nuclear explosions or steady rocket blasts. Science fiction writer Larry Niven has remarked that if the dinosaurs had had a space programme, they would still be around today.

However, it is not the threat of the NEAs that interests us here, but their promise.

We can reach the NEAs. Already asteroid Eros has been orbited by an unmanned spacecraft. And surprisingly, perhaps, some of the NEAs come so close to Earth that it would take less fuel to reach them and return than it takes to get to the surface of the Moon and back. The catch is that it takes much *longer* to get to a NEA than the Moon – and, paradoxically, the closer the NEA comes to Earth's orbit, the longer a mission might take. Earth and a NEA in a nearby orbit circle the sun like the two hands of a great cosmic clock, running slightly out of sync; it can take a long time between the moments when they come close to each other.

Even so, round-trip mission plans of a year or so to candidate NEAs have been drawn up. Humans have survived in space for longer than this – all of them Russians, aboard the Mir space station. But, of course, we have yet to learn how to run a spacecraft independent of resupply from Earth for such a period. And it would take hundreds of days to run home in the event of an emergency, compared to just three days from the Moon.

Still, voyages to NEAs are intermediate in difficulty between missions to the Moon and to Mars, and perhaps will provide a stepping-stone in our expansion into the Solar System.

However, NEAs are more than just training grounds for Mars trips. The NEAs themselves could prove to be very valuable prizes indeed.

Some NEAs are flying mountains of natural steel and precious metals, such as gold and platinum: a single metallic-type near-Earth object would be worth, conservatively, trillions of dollars in today's market. It would be so valuable, in fact, that it would change the market itself.

The prospect of reaching what is known as a C-type asteroid is even more exciting. Because the C-types contain water.

Imagine you are a prospector reaching a C-type near-Earth asteroid: a ball of loosely aggregated dirt, probably eighty per cent silicate rocks, sixteen per cent water, two per cent carbon, two per cent metals. This is an extraordinarily rich resource. But how can you exploit it?

The first thing to make on the asteroid is rocket fuel, a methane-oxygen bipropellant. You crack asteroid water with electrolysis. You may remember this process from school science experiments with Pyrex beakers and wires and batteries: to break water down into hydrogen and oxygen, all you have to do is to pass an electric current through it. (There is no shortage of solar power; you are no further from the sun than Earth.) On the NEA the electrolysis units will be somewhat more advanced, perhaps consisting of sandwiched layers of electrolyte-impregnated plastic separated by metal meshes. Such units have been used extensively on nuclear submarines and are planned for use on the International Space Station. They run for thousands of hours without maintenance.

That gives you your oxygen. As for the methane for your rocket fuel, this can be extracted directly from the asteroid material, where it occurs naturally, or by processing carbon dioxide using a piece of equipment called a Sabatier reactor. These reactors are very efficient, ninety-nine per cent efficient in fact, and exothermic, which means they require no input of heat to make them work – just the presence of a ruthenium catalyst. Sabatier units have also been used in space before, for life-support applications. They have been tested by NASA and the US Air Force, and are planned for use on the Space Station.

Methane-oxygen is not the most powerful chemical propellant – the optimum is oxygen-hydrogen, used in the Saturn rockets and the Space Shuttle. But hydrogen is difficult to liquefy and store: it requires very low temperatures, and, being so light, is very bulky. Methane, by comparison, is like oxygen – a soft cryogenic, capable of being stored in liquid form at relatively high temperatures.

All this sounds exotic. But this is very robust engineering, gaslight era stuff, technologies centuries old. It's just a novel application.

Once you have your rocket propellant you start bagging up permafrost water from the asteroid, along with a little unprocessed asteroid material. You use your propellant to start firing water back to Earth orbit, specifically a type of orbit called HEEO, a highly eccentric Earth orbit, which in terms of accessibility is a good compromise place to store extraterrestrial materials.

This will not be a complex operation. The methane rockets are based on tried and trusted designs, and the cargo carriers will be little more than plastic bags wrapped around big dirty ice cubes. Mining an asteroid is easy.

But in HEEO this water will become unimaginably precious. The reason is the vast cost of using rockets to haul a comparable mass up from Earth's surface. And this is your competitive advantage. With your pipeline to Earth in place, you start to get rich. Very rich indeed.

It doesn't end there. With suitable engineering, you can extract from your asteroid dirt not just water but also carbon dioxide, nitrogen, sulphur, ammonia, phosphates – all the requirements of a life-support system. You can also use the asteroid dirt to make glass, fibreglass, ceramics, concrete, soil to grow things in.

And you can further process the dirt to extract its metals. The result will be around ninety per cent iron, seven per cent nickel, one per cent cobalt, and traces. That trace, however, includes platinum, which, being so precious, may be the first resource returned to the surface of the Earth; nickel and cobalt will probably follow.

Later you might start the construction of a solar power plant in Earth orbit. The design would make the most efficient use of the resources available. The high-technology components of the plant, such as guidance, control, communications, power conversion and microwave transmission systems, will be assembled on Earth. The massive low-tech components – wires, cables, girders, bolts, fixtures, station-keeping propellants and solar cells – will all be manufactured in space from asteroid materials. This plan reduces the mass that will have to be lifted into Earth orbit several-fold. Your plant will produce energy – safe, clean, pollution-free – that you can sell back to Earth.

With such a scheme, within a few years asteroid volatiles could support Earth-orbital habitats, missions to the Moon and Mars, and supply raw materials and power for Earth.

A crewed mission to a NEA could even establish a colony. This will be self-sufficient, almost from day one.

Schemes to exploit the NEAs are approaching the feasibility of business plans; already several hard-headed entrepreneurs are considering ways to reach out to the mines in the sky.

Personally I remain a fan of the Moon as our first destination: the Moon is much easier to get to, is only three days from home, and is much bigger than any asteroid besides. But I have to admit that the Moon is a much poorer resource. What is left over from asteroid ore after you extract the water and volatiles and metals – the stuff any self-respecting miner would throw away – that *slag* is about equivalent to the richest Moon rocks.

The riches of the near-Earth asteroids, especially their water, should fund our first expansion off Earth. But only for a time, and maybe not as long as you think.

What then?

Chapter 15

The Mighty Thirst

Every living thing is a sort of imperialist, seeking to transform as much as possible of its environment into itself.

— Bertrand Russell

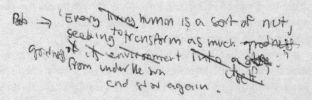

Let us think hard about the growth of the human population, and what it means for our far future.

There are only three possibilities for the future of mankind:

First, we may become extinct.

Second, our numbers may stabilise, or gently decline; we will survive an indefinitely long time, but our demands for resources will plateau or decline.

Third, our numbers may grow.

In a sense, there is little distinction between the second and third of these possibilities. Bluntly speaking, the sun is going to go out and we will have to find somewhere else to live, or die with it. The only difference between the cases of growth and not-growth is how quickly we reach the point of exceeding the carrying capacity of our Earth and its Solar System.

So how quickly *are* we growing?

The growth rate of the human population on Earth, historically, has been two per cent a year. That doesn't sound much, but it is an exponential growth, working like compound interest. At that rate our population doubles every thirty-five years, an increase by tenfold every century or so.

Think about what that means. In two centuries the increase is a hundredfold; after three centuries, a thousand. Exponential growth is relentless, and always seems faster than you think.

At the time of writing there are already *six* billion people on the planet. Can we imagine six *thousand* billion on Earth in the year 2300? Of course not.

In the best case, how many people could Earth hold? Ten, twenty billion?

We have talked of moving into space. How long do you think it would take for an expansionist, growing species to eat up a Solar System? Millions of years, perhaps?

It turns out that the *whole* of the inner Solar System out to Mars – planets, near-Earth asteroids and all – could supply only enough water for maybe fifty billion people. And it might take us no more than a century or two to reach those numbers.

Happily, there is more water in the outer Solar System – a *lot* more.

There are a vast number of asteroids in the main belt, orbiting between Mars and Jupiter: perhaps ten *billion* larger than a hundred metres in diameter, and a hundred billion between ten and a hundred metres across. They are rich in water, metals, phosphates, carbon, nitrogen, sulphur. We think the main-belt asteroids could contribute about half the water available on Earth, vastly expanding mankind's opportunities for growth.

The main belt may not be the most interesting territory to open up, however.

The asteroids tend to occur in groups, shepherded by orbital resonances with the planets. Some of the most significant groups, beyond the main belt itself, are known as the Trojan asteroids. These cluster in Jupiter's orbit at the so-called Lagrange points, points of gravitational stability.

The Trojans are comparatively close together. By comparison, the belt asteroids are spread over an orbit wider than that of Mars, so it's much easier to travel between the Trojans. And the Trojan asteroids are rich: it is believed that the asteroid mass available in the Trojans is several times greater than that in the main belt itself. Not only that, they seem to be super-carbonaceous. They are made of the same stuff as C-type asteroids and comet nuclei, but in different, more volatile-rich proportions. It was *cold* out there where the giant planets formed, cold enough for the lighter stuff to stick.

Some analysts think the Trojans might prove to be the richest resource pool in the Solar System . . . and the Trojans are far from the limit of the system's riches.

Beyond the asteroid belt circle the outer planets – Jupiter, Saturn, Uranus and Neptune – and their retinues of moons.

Out there, in the stillness and cold and dark, the worlds that were spawned were not like Earth. The remote planets grew immense, misty, stuffed with light elements like hydrogen and helium that were boiled out of the worlds that formed close to the sun's heat. And some of their moons are little more than giant balls of water, frozen into ice.

The archetypal ice moon is perhaps Jupiter's fourth moon, Callisto.

At the orbit of Jupiter, five times as far as Earth from the central light, the sun is shrunk to the tiniest of discs. And, through this rectilinear, reduced light, Callisto swims.

It is like a dark, misty twin of Earth's Moon. Its surface is crowded with craters – even more so than the Moon's, for there are none of the giant lava-flood seas that smooth over much lunar terrain. The largest craters are complex structures, plains of pale ice surrounded by multiple arcs of folded and cracked land, like ripples frozen into shattered ice and rock. Some of these features are the size of continents, large enough to stretch around this lonely moon's curved horizon, evidently the results of immense, terrifying impacts.

But these great geological sculptures are oddly smoothed out, the cracks and ripples reduced to shallow ridges. Unlike the Moon, Callisto is made of rock and water ice. Over billions of years ice suffers 'viscous relaxation'; it flows and slumps. The ancient craters subsided, like great geological sighs, leaving spectacular palimpsests.

Save for surface impacts, nothing much has happened to Callisto since it accreted from the greater cloud that formed the Jupiter system. Jupiter's inner moons – Io, Europa, Ganymede – have been heated, to one degree or another, by tidal pumping by the mother planet Jupiter. So Europa, under a crust of ice, appears to have a liquid ocean (which may shelter life); and Io has been driven by that perennial squeezing to spectacular volcanism.

Callisto was born too far from her huge parent for such gravitational succour. Here, the only heat is a relic of primordial radioactivity; here there is no geology, no volcanism, no hidden ocean.

But there is a change on Callisto – even weather, of a sort.

Walking on the surface you would find a thin smearing of black dust over the dirty white of the underlying ice; the dust is loose, fine grains. The dust is here because ice sublimes, shrivelling away, just a metre every ten million years – but it leaves the dust behind. The ice gathers on the north side of the great crater walls, because it is a shade colder there. This thin scraping is a ten-million-year frost, the *only* action on Callisto.

A single ice moon, like Callisto, has around *forty times* as much water as Earth's oceans.

Overall there is much more water in the asteroids and the outer system moons than in Earth's oceans – several hundred times as much – perhaps enough to support ten thousand *trillion* human beings. It is a huge number, but only six exponential-growth tenfold jumps away from ten billion. If we keep growing it might take only six or seven centuries to swell to that mighty number. And then what?

Luckily, even the outer planets and their moons are not the limit of the Solar System's inventory of water.

The last planet to be discovered is the most remote: Pluto, found in 1930. We know now that this is a double world, for Pluto has a companion moon, called Charon. Their separation is only fourteen of Pluto's diameters. The worlds are strikingly different in hue, with Pluto a blood red, Charon ice blue.

It would be strange indeed to stand on the surface of Pluto. The sun is five light-hours away, a bright pinpoint. Unless the insulation of your spacesuit is perfect, your leaked heat sends nitrogen clouds hissing around your footsteps, and where you walk you burn craters in the ice. Gravity is only a few per cent of Earth's, and you feel as if you might blow away. There are clouds above you of wispy cirrus: aerosol clusters suspended in an atmosphere of nitrogen and methane.

The best tourist viewpoint on Pluto is surely the sub-Charon point. From there, the moon hangs directly over your head, a misty blue disc, six times the size of the Moon as seen from Earth.

Like the Moon, Charon is tidally locked to its parent, and keeps the same face to Pluto as it orbits. But, unlike Earth, Pluto is also locked to its twin. Every six days the worlds turn about each other, facing each other constantly, like two waltzers. Pluto-Charon is the only significant system we know of in which both partners are tidally locked.

Pluto, like its moon-twin, is a ball of rock clad with thick mantles of water ice and nitrogen ice, laced with methane, ammonia and organic compounds. It is like a big, stable comet nucleus that barely deserves the status of 'planet': there are moons bigger than Pluto.

It is now believed that Pluto is but one of a whole cloud of similar objects, ice worldlets and massive comets, circling silently in the dark. The cloud's inner margins are forty times as far as Earth is from the sun, and its outer limits may extend some hundred thousand times as far. That's halfway to the nearest star. The cloud may contain as many as one hundred trillion comets, and may mass as much as *ten times* all the planets in the Solar System combined.

It is almost impossible to imagine a future mankind grown so vast that we need to take on that great dark pit of outer comets and worldlets. By then we will have consumed the inner worlds and moons and asteroids, greedily drinking the Solar System's water. We will, in fact, have turned a substantial fraction of the system's resources into copies of ourselves.

*

•

Of course our growth may not continue at its present rate – or it may not continue at all.

Perhaps we will limit our numbers more or less voluntarily, through contraception or even sterilisation programmes, or simply through social change as we have seen in some developed nations already, where population growth is below replacements levels. Or perhaps as we approach the carrying capacity of the Earth, disease or war will take their toil.

But perhaps not. We have been growing at that two per cent figure, more or less, throughout our history.

And there is an iron logic at work: if we keep growing – *no matter what the pace of growth* – we must reach the point of exhaustion of *any* given resource pool, sooner or later. If we continue to grow, we will at last be forced to look beyond the Solar System.

And even if we stand still we can't win, for we must eventually face the death of the sun itself.

Facing that far-distant calamity, some of us may seek refuge on the most remarkable moon of all.

Chapter 16

The Last Refuge

> O God! I could be bounded in a nutshell, and count
> myself a king of infinite space, were it not that I have
> bad dreams.
>
> — **William Shakespeare**

ere is a bad dream indeed.

To begin at the beginning:

Our sun is a second-generation star. It formed from a spinning cloud of rock and snow: mostly primordial hydrogen and helium born in the Big Bang, polluted by silicon, carbon and oxygen, elements manufactured by the first stars, the oldest in the universe. The cloud has twice the mass of the final sun, and was a hundred times the width of our present Solar System.

Disturbed by a supernova shock wave, the cloud collapsed, and spun faster. It heated up, became unstable, and broke up into successively smaller fragments.

Eventually the core was so hot that hydrogen nuclei there began to fuse to helium. When fusion began, the thermonuclear energy generated balanced the inward gravitational force. The core stopped contracting.

Thus, our sun was born.

The rest of the nebula condensed into dust particles and snow-flakes. The orbiting particles collided with each other, stuck, and formed a flat disc of swarming planetesimals. The planetesimals collided further; some grew in size, forming the planets, and others fragmented.

Earth formed quickly, deep in the hostile maw of the new sun's gravity well.

Further out, it was cold enough for ices to form: of water, carbon dioxide, ammonia and methane. So while the inner planets were dominated by rock, the accreting planetesimals beyond swept up a great deal of dirty snow as well as dust. Gigantic, gaseous planets began to coalesce.

One of them was Saturn.

Around Saturn, a new accretion disc gathered, like a scale model of the solar disc. Saturn's giant moon Titan – and the other ice moons, and the rings – grew out of a mixture of water ice, silicates, ammonia, methane and other trace elements.

Titan was half rock, half ice. A giant among moons, its huge mass caused it to heat as it collapsed. The primordial ices were melted and vaporised. The rock settled to the centre, because of its greater density. Thus, Titan is a ball of silicate rock, overlaid by a shell of water ice.

Titan's first ocean was a mixture of ammonia and methane. A dense atmosphere was raised. The new world was a cauldron, with searing temperatures and air pressure hundreds of times its present level.

It was, remarkably, like a twin of young Earth.

But, over the next hundred million years, the fate of the two worlds diverged.

Titan's new ocean and atmosphere were not stable. Ultraviolet flux from the young sun beat down on the atmosphere, shattering its ammonia molecules; planetesimals continued to fall, blasting away swathes of Titan's atmosphere; and more atmospheric gases were dissolved in the oceans.

Born too far from the sun, Titan descended into an epochal freeze . . .

But this strange, remote world may prove to be a pivot of

humanity's future, and perhaps our last refuge when the sun itself dies.

Titan is Saturn's largest moon: larger than Mercury, more massive than Pluto. It is the only moon with a significant atmosphere. If it wasn't in orbit around Saturn, we would surely regard it as a planet in its own right. And in October 1997, NASA and the ESA launched Cassini-Huygens: a Saturn orbiter carrying a Titan lander, to arrive in 2004. (The lander, Huygens, was named for astronomer Christiaan Huygens, who, in addition to making the first useful drawing of Mars, discovered Titan.)

If you could ride with Huygens, you would land on a dark and murky world, covered in purple slush.

The lander has come down in a shallow depression. Towards the horizon there are rolling hills. The horizon itself is lost in gloom and haze. The peaks are stained dark red and yellow, with splashes of ochre on their flanks, and streaks of grey, exposed water-ice at the higher elevations. There are scars in the hills' profiles, left by recent icefalls. The profiles look oddly softened: these are mountains of ice, not rock. Clouds, red and orange, swirl above the hills. The clouds are fat methane cumuli, fifteen or twenty kilometres high, oppressive.

It is dark. Hidden beyond the kilometres of smog, the distant sun has only a hundredth of its brightness at Earth's distance: it is like a dim twilight on Earth, and any explorers should pack flashlights. And, just as the smog hides the surface from us, so the sky is hidden from the ground – the rings of Saturn are forever invisible from Titan's surface.

But there are compensations. Titan has thick air but light gravity. On Titan you could strap on wings and fly like a bird, under your own muscle power.

That thick layer of air is actually *double* the mass of Earth's atmosphere, exerting fifty per cent more pressure. The atmosphere is mostly nitrogen (like Earth's), with some methane, argon and hydrogen. The atmosphere is laden with haze, formed by particles the size of those in cigarette smoke.

The temperature is a mere ninety-four K, nearly two hundred degrees below the freezing point of water. But the deep cold is the reason such a small world has been able to cling onto its air.

Since its Earth-like birth, Titan's atmosphere has been shaped by billions of years of chemistry. Titan has virtually no magnetic field of its own, unlike Earth, so the sun's ultraviolet, the solar wind and magnetospheric plasma from Saturn all attack the upper atmosphere. The ultraviolet destroys upper atmosphere methane, which then combines with nitrogen to form complex molecules: hydrocarbons, made of carbon and hydrogen atoms, such as natural gas, petroleum and waxes; and nitriles, compounds containing nitrogen atoms such as hydrogen cyanide – deadly for us, but crucially involved in the steps on Earth that led to life.

The hydrocarbons cluster in complex organic solids called 'tholins' ('tholin' is Greek for 'mud'). The tholins drift as orange-brown smog in the upper atmosphere, giving the clouds their characteristic autumnal colours, and they rain steadily down onto the land. And they've been doing it for four billion years: long enough for a layer of muddy slush to accumulate over the bone-hard ice, perhaps hundreds of metres thick.

Thus, Titan has become a world of ice and organic slush and haze.

We can't see Titan's surface, as it is perpetually hidden by the hazy atmosphere. But recent Hubble Space Telescope infrared observations suggest there is a huge 'continent' dominating the hemisphere that leads as Titan orbits. Perhaps this is comparable to Mars's Tharsis Bulge, a continent-sized region of geological uplift.

There are other, more indirect clues to Titan's hidden geography. The air should be depleted of methane in ten million years, by photochemical processes that destroy methane in the upper atmosphere. But Titan is a lot older than that, and it still has methane. So the methane must be replenished somehow.

We think Titan has seas – liquid hydrocarbon, seas of ethane – with methane dissolved in them. The seas would work as the source of the methane. (And on Titan, you could go sailing on petrol seas.) But there's still a problem.

The orbit of Titan is elliptical. So, even though Titan rotates to keep the same face to Saturn, any surface liquid is going to slosh backwards and forwards: tides. This implies a dissipation of energy by tidal friction, which means the circularisation of the orbit. So we need an ocean to explain the methane; but with a big ocean, there should be a circular orbit.

Because of this paradox, the Cassini mission planners don't know what they are sending Huygens into. They have designed the heroic little probe to float, or to sink in a less dense ocean, or to land in slush.

Some suggest that the most likely resolution is that Titan is like a flooded Moon. Despite its thick atmosphere, Titan's surface must be covered with impact craters, up to a couple of hundred kilometres across. Perhaps the crater floors are filled with circular lakes of liquid hydrocarbons. Some would have central peaks, protruding from the organic washes. The crater seas may be big enough to serve as methane reservoirs, but in bodies of fluid that size the tidal friction should be negligible.

And there is rain on Titan, of ethane and methane. The huge, slow-moving droplets evaporate before they reach ground level. But the rain should wash the tholins off the elevated ground. So the peaks of the mountains will be exposed water ice.

Thus, like Earth, Titan has air and lakes and rain. But fundamentally Titan is *not* like Earth. Its 'bedrock' is water ice. There may be methane geysers, plate tectonics, even volcanoes. But these are driven by ammonia-water processes, deep in the icy mantle: 'cryovolcanism'.

On Titan, you would be an ultra-hot monster, your body hundreds of degrees hotter than molten lava.

But, as we have said, when they were young, Titan and Earth were much more alike.

The first living things on Earth were cruder than the most humble microbe alive today, just barely able to make copies of themselves. But those first creatures arose in a soup of prebiotic chemicals, prelife organic molecules. The most important organics are amino acids, the building blocks of proteins, and nucleotide bases, the building blocks of nucleic acids. These prebiotic components must, of course, have formed on a pre-Genesis Earth.

On primaeval Titan, too, there was plenty of energy to drive complex organic chemistry, just as there is today. And therefore young Titan was probably also a factory for prebiotic chemicals, the building blocks of life.

And perhaps life formed there too. Perhaps those primaeval life forms even reached a high degree of complexity. But no Earth-like life could have survived, as Titan settled into its billion-year freeze.

Titan's deep cold has a number of subtle effects. At high temperature, organic molecules fall to pieces. On Titan, even the oldest organic molecules might still be present, in the deepest slush layers: thus Titan's surface is coated in deep-frozen primaeval soup, as if the moon is a fossil of ancient Earth.

So Titan, at the very least, will be a fascinating organic chemistry laboratory, offering us a deep insight into the fundamental processes which shaped life on Earth. But Titan may have a value far beyond the scientific.

Titan may be a key resource in our future exploration and development of the Solar System. It is an organic-synthesis machine, way off in the outer system. It could become a factory, churning out fibres, food, any organic-chemistry product – even CHON food, manufactured from carbon, hydrogen, oxygen, nitrogen. Generally the comets have been suggested as an off-Earth resource for such raw materials. Titan is a lot closer than most comets, and has vastly more mass besides.

Further out in time, it may be possible to export Titan's volatiles to inner planets lacking them. An Earth-like biosphere needs nitrogen. Mars, for example, has little nitrogen; Titan has plenty, and it would be relatively easily extracted from the moon's shallow gravity well. Titan nitrogen could be used to terraform Mars.

Titan – cold, dark and remote – may seem a less obvious candidate for colonisation than the Moon or Mars. But Titan is a vital resource pool on the fringe of interstellar space, and only on Titan can we detect, in the present day, the complex organic chemistry which characterises Earth. A beachhead on Titan could be the key to the mysteries of our own past, to the outer Solar System – even to the stars.

And as the life of the Solar System itself draws to a close, Titan may prove our final resting place.

The sun's gravity tends to pull it inwards. But this tendency to collapse is countered by a continuing fusion explosion at the sun's core. Happily for us, radiation and gravity are in balance – for now.

But, throughout its history, as its core becomes clogged with accumulated helium ash, the sun has been slowly imploding. The energy released by this gradual contraction has led to the sun slowly brightening, getting about one per cent warmer every hundred million years.

For billions of years life on Earth has been able to cope with this slow drift. Despite the changes in the sun the planet's surface temperature has been kept largely unchanging, thanks to matter and energy feedback cycles maintained by living and geological processes.

But this can't last for ever.

At present about one per cent of Earth's atmosphere is made up of water vapour, and very little of it is to be found in the stratosphere, the atmosphere's upper levels; nearly all the evaporated water condenses into clouds and rains out before it gets that high.

But as the temperature rises inexorably, more water will evaporate from the oceans. Water vapour is very effective at trapping the sun's heat, and so the surface of Earth will be warmed further. In a billion years or so, the atmosphere will contain about ten per cent water, and the temperature will reach sixty Celsius. By now the air will be so warm and wet that not all the evaporated water will condense as rain; significant amounts of it will start to wander up into the stratosphere. And there, far above the protection of the ozone layer, ultraviolet radiation will break water molecules apart, releasing hydrogen that will escape to space.

The beginning of the loss of Earth's water, as if a plug has been pulled, will be a disaster.

And, even as the water disappears, still the temperature will climb. One species after another will come up against what the biologists call thermal barriers to their survival, and the planet will shed the evolutionary complexity it painfully gained over billions of years. The end will come at last at a temperature at which the very stuff of life – the giant biomolecules – is broken down.

This grim vision is just a billion years away. But life on Earth originated some four billion years ago, soon after the rocks cooled and the oceans formed. We should not think of Earth as a young world; already we have lived through *four-fifths* of its habitable lifetime.

After that, things will get even worse.

Our oceans will boil, and huge clouds of vapour will be suspended in the atmosphere; a powerful greenhouse factor will drive temperatures higher still, ever faster. About a hundred million years after that, *all* Earth's water will be lost. Earth will be left baked dry, its surface cracked and flattened under a dense, sluggish atmosphere, utterly lifeless.

Water is essential in maintaining Earth's greater equilibrium. For example, carbon dioxide is continually injected into Earth's atmosphere by tectonic processes, as carbon-rich rock is dragged down into the mantle and melted. But the wind and the rain weather silicate rocks into limestone, binding carbon dioxide from the atmosphere as they do so. When all the water has gone there will be no way the carbon dioxide can be bound back into the rocks. As a result carbon dioxide levels in the air will soar, leading to a further massive greenhouse pulse that will raise the world's temperature by several hundred degrees. And sulphur oxides that were once washed out of the air by the rain will stay there, making the atmosphere acid; it will be a grisly rerun of the evolution of Venus. It will be a grim irony if, in this late day, Earth and Venus at last become true twins.

Meanwhile, over four billion more years, the slow death of the sun will continue.

When all the hydrogen in the core is consumed, the ancient balance between radiation and gravity will fail. The core will collapse, and nuclear fusion will begin in the hydrogen in the outer edges of the sun, causing it to expand.

At last the star's expansion will result in a vast, misty red giant, a glowing cloud that will consume Mercury and Venus. Earth might be spared this fate; by then the sun will have lost a quarter of its mass to the streaming solar wind, and the ties of gravity will bind Earth loosely, so that it will circle further away, perhaps close to the present orbit of Mars. But there will be no respite from the scorching heat. The sun will span the sky, and on Earth the land will be hot enough to melt lead.

But the changes in the sun that will wreck Earth will bring warmth to Titan.

The brown smog that swathes Titan is caused by the sun's ultraviolet light. This shines onto the methane and ammonia in the air, and makes the complex organic molecules that clog the atmosphere and rain slowly down to the surface.

But the red giant sun of the future will produce much less ultraviolet. Titan's haze will thin, the tholins rain out – and the clouds will clear, for the first time in ten billion years.

In the new sunlight, the ethane lakes will boil. The gases trapped there – nitrogen, methane, hydrogen – will be pumped out of the evaporating liquid, thickening the atmosphere. Eventually the ice shells over the ancient ammonia oceans will melt. Ammonia and water vapour will enrich the air still further. And the ancient organic compounds will fall into a water-rich ocean.

Thus, for a brief period, Titan will have new lakes and oceans, not of hydrocarbons, but *of liquid water*. For a time, Titan might be Earth-like: a refuge for humanity perhaps, fleeing the rubble of Earth.

But this will be a brief respite. As the sun continues to balloon, the last of Titan's ice will melt, and those new oceans will boil away. Then, after a few million years at best, nothing will be left of Titan but its rocky core.

*

The sun's evolution will continue. Starved of hydrogen fuel, it will begin to burn whatever is available, even helium ash, and the heavier elements that result. Briefly the sun will burn bright again, two or three times as bright as today. It will be a brief Indian summer, as the flaring sun illuminates the dispersing cloud of debris that surrounds it.

But soon the sun will subside into a fading white dwarf, the last of its fuel consumed, and night will close on the ruins of the Solar System.

Our journey away from Earth, which began with tentative foot-steps on our nearest neighbour the Moon, has taken us to all the sun's planets and far beyond. Perhaps we will grow to a mighty host and consume them all; perhaps not.

But whatever we do, twilight must at last fall over all our sister worlds. And long before that final night, we humans will be forced to make a choice: to submit at last to extinction – or to become nomads among the stars.

FOUR

•

Pilots of the Purple Twilight

Maxine to Albert with B+J ~~see~~ go behind brush.

Look at the fires! Look, look up the sky!
Look at all the fire – folk standing in the air! ✓ ←
Their bright bodies, burning there!

Chapter 17

An Ocean of Suns

Look at the stars! Look, look, up at the sky!
O look at all the fire-folk sitting in the air!
The bright boroughs, the circle-citadels there!
— **Gerald Manley Hopkins**

To explore appears to be an ancient human imperative.

The story of the Polynesians, who with little more than Stone Age technology covered the far-scattered islands of the Pacific, is well known. Modern Western civilisation has given us the epic voyages of James Cook, Neil Armstrong, and many others. But the drive to seek out and explore may even predate our species; one of our evolutionary forebears, *Homo Erectus*, appears to have walked throughout the old world a million years ago.

And now we stand on the shore of a new ocean: an ocean of suns, stretching across the abyss all around us. This new ocean will present us with a challenge unprecedented in our history – a challenge which may even lead to our remaking as a species.

But the sun is dying. If we wish to survive, if we continue to struggle against extinction, it is a challenge we must one day accept.

The very first interstellar journey we are likely to make will be to our sun's nearest neighbour.

To get there you travel a mere four light years – that is, it would

•

143

take a ray of light four years to get there. Mere? – but it is an immense distance by any modern comparison, a hundred *million* times further than the Apollo astronauts' lunar journeys.

But if you look around the sky, surprisingly, the constellations are little changed.

The constellations are patterns formed by a view of a three-dimensional assemblage of stars from a particular point in space. If you move across interstellar distances, your viewpoint shifts so much that the patterns would distort, the lamps scattered through the sky swimming past like harbour lights.

But the stars of the Orion constellation, for example, aren't close together; they are scattered through a volume of space a thousand light years deep, and the nearest of them is no closer than *five hundred* light years from the sun. So after four light years Orion is scarcely changed; you have not come far, not compared to the distance to Orion's giant suns.

Here, your sky is dominated by two sun-like stars, bound close together. This is Alpha Centauri, a bright double star. And somewhere in the complex sky around you is Proxima, the third star in the system, orbiting the main binary pair four hundred times further away from those twins than they are from each other. Proxima is actually the closest star of all to Sol, but it is an unspectacular red dwarf, a minor component of this system.

Alpha Centauri: the dream of centuries, the first port of call beyond Pluto's realm, a name that has resonated through a hundred starship studies, and a thousand dreams. And it is a promising destination.

Each of the two central suns looks hauntingly like our sun, but they are only a few light-hours apart. If the brighter star, Alpha A, were in place of the sun, its companion, Alpha B, would be within the Solar System: closer than planet Neptune, in fact. On an Earth-like planet circling A, the companion would be a brilliant star in the sky, bright enough to cast sharp shadows; in fact it would show a disc to a sharp enough naked eye. There would be double sunrises, double sunsets, strange eclipses of one star by the other; the sky would be a bright and complex place.

144

And perhaps there are planets like Earth orbiting A and B. We used to think that multiple star systems couldn't grow planetary systems because of the stars' gravitational perturbations. But for planets as close to Alpha A as Earth is to the sun, B's gravity would have no significant effect on orbital stability – or, earlier, on the formation of inner rocky worlds.

So Alpha Centauri may not just be a twin star. It may be a twin Solar System: a place where humans might have evolved on a planet all but indistinguishable from Earth, even with the same constellations – but with a whole other planetary system a few light-hours away, so close humans might already have been able to complete interstellar journeys.

Distant planets may follow more exotic trajectories than anything in our Solar System. A planet could even inhabit both systems, looping on decades-long trajectories back and forth between the two stars. But within a few million years, as the stars follow their own elliptical orbits around each other, such a planet would probably be flung out into the dark, from whence, perhaps, it came.

And the mutual influence of A and B on each other would probably prevent the formation of large planets much further out from each star than Earth's orbit. All the volatile material that was absorbed into our great gas giants would here be left unconsolidated, drifting in huge clouds of asteroids around the stars. There are no Jupiters here, but there are a *lot* more asteroids.

In Sol's domain, the asteroids have been shepherded by the planets into the simple ring-shaped belts between Mars and Jupiter, or else they cluster in clouds trailing or preceding the giant planets, like the Trojans gathered at Jupiter's points of gravitational stability. But here the orbital mechanics are much more complex. Alpha's asteroid clouds probably extend right across the space between the stars, forming knots and bands and figure-of-eight loops, even what look like spokes radiating from each star's central system: clouds of density marked out by the sweeping paths of flocks of asteroids, each tugged by the competing pulls of the stars and their retinues of planets.

Perhaps there are hazards here; those inner planets must be subject to a higher rate of bombardment from space than Sol's planets. But from an Earth orbiting Alpha A or B, there would be a line of light across the sky: dazzling, alluring, the sparkle of trillions of asteroids, the promise of unimaginable wealth. It would be as if somebody dismantled Jupiter and turned it into convenient clouds of asteroid mines.

The Solar System is impoverished by comparison. *This* is where the action is in our part of space: Alpha Centauri, a double-star system with a sky full of flying mines to boot. Reaching this powerful, rich stellar system would galvanise our civilisation.

But if you look back the way you came, you see a compact constellation that is hauntingly familiar. That W shape is surely Cassiopeia, one of the most easily recognisable of our star figures, but there is an extra star to the left of the pattern, turning the constellation into a crude zigzag.

That star is our sun: just a point of pale yellow light, bright, but not exceptionally so. And the sun, the Earth and all the planets could be eclipsed by a grain of sand.

Our sun is just one star in an ocean of four hundred billion stars, a great spiral system called the Galaxy.

Imagine travelling out of the Galaxy's disc, through thirty or forty thousand light years.

The Galaxy is a ceiling of curdled light that spans the sky. The main disc of stars is flatter and thinner than you might have expected, in proportion to its width no thicker than a few sheets of paper. There are strata in that disc: a central sheet of swarming blue stars and dust lanes is sandwiched between dimmer, older stars. The core, bulging out of the plane of the disc like an egg yolk, is a compact mass of yellowish light; but the core is not spherical, rather markedly elliptical.

The spiral arms are fragmented. They are a delicate blue laced with ruby-red nebulae and the blue-white blaze of individual stars – a granularity of light – and with dark lanes traced between each arm.

Here and there you can see flashes of light, blisters of gas that are supernova explosions.

The whole system is immense: some hundred thousand light years in diameter, so vast that a signal from the Galaxy's far side travelling at the speed of light, launched when humanity first evolved in southern Africa, would only now be completing a single span of the disc.

But the familiar disc – shining core, spiral arms – is actually embedded in a broader, spherical mass of dim red stars. Here and there you can see great clusters in that sullen mass, swarms of crimson fireflies, each of which must contain millions of stars.

When we look out at the Galaxy from Earth, we are looking into the plane of the disc – which is why we see the Galaxy as the 'Milky Way', a stripe of cloudy light across the night sky. Nevertheless we have been able to map the Galaxy's structure, to some extent, by studying radio emissions and other forms of radiation that penetrate the intervening clouds of stars and dust.

We know that the Galaxy is dominated by two giant spiral arms that appear to emerge from the core: they are called the Sagittarius Arm and the Outer Arm, broad, coherent lanes that sweep outwards from close to that central bulge, out to the rim of the Galaxy. These two great arms define the Galaxy, each of them wrapping right around the core before dispersing at the rim into a mist of shining stars and glowing nebulae and brooding black clouds. The other 'arms' are really just fragments, and our sun, along with Alpha Centauri, is embedded in one of those unspectacular scattered fragments, about a quarter of the way out from the centre.

The Galaxy rotates, slowly. It takes two hundred million years to complete a turn. The stars swarm, following individual orbits around the Galaxy core, like a school of sparkling fish. And the spiral arms are evolving too, ridges of light sparking with young stars, churning their way through the disc of the Galaxy. But the arms are just wave formations, like the bunching of traffic jams, with individual stars swimming through the regions of greatest brightness.

The Galaxy's oldest stars are to be found in the halo, the spherical cloud around the main disc. And the stars in the core are old too.

They formed early in the Galaxy's history: today the survivors are very ancient, late in their evolution.

Most of the star formation going on now is happening in the spiral arms. The stars condense out of the 'interstellar medium', which is a rich, complex mix of gas and dust clouds. The key turns out to be the supernovas. These great explosions blow bubbles of hot plasma, hundreds of light years across, in the interstellar medium. The supernova shock waves enrich the medium with heavy molecules – carbon, oxygen, iron – manufactured inside the stars, and each explosion kicks off another wave of star formation. It was just such an explosion that triggered the formation of our own Solar System.

Each exploding supernova in turn creates a few new giant stars, a few more supernovas – which stir up the medium and create more stars, at a controlled rate. So it goes, a feedback loop, with supernova explosions as the catalyst, generations of stars ending in cooling dwarfs or black holes. The spiral arms are actually waves of stellar formation, lit up by their shortest-lived, brightest stars.

The Galaxy is no mere cloud of stars. It appears to be a self-regulating system of a hundred billion stars, in fact the largest organised system we know of. It is a factory for making stars – or rather, an ecology.

Imagine leaving Earth and sun and travelling, in some magical starship, towards the constellation of Sagittarius – towards the centre of the Galaxy.

Our sun is in the middle of a 'bubble' in space, hundreds of light years across. The bubble is a more tenuous vacuum blown into the galactic medium by an ancient supernova explosion. Soon you pass out of the local bubble into a neighbouring void the astronomers called Loop One.

If you look back to the sun, it is probably already lost against a crowded background. But you might make out a great sheet of stars that slices through the galactic plane, right past Sol. The astronomers call it Gould's Belt, a sheet of the brightest, youngest stars in Earth's sky.

When you look ahead, there is a band of darkness. You are

reaching the inner limit of our spiral arm, looking into the rift between the arms, the dense dark clouds there.

Emerging from these clouds you see a new river of stars: stars that are varied, yellow and blue and orange, and the river is crammed with giant dark clouds and brilliant shining nebulae.

You have passed out of the spiral arm which contains the sun (and Alpha Centauri), which is anyhow just a shingle, a short arc. *This* mighty flow is the next arm in, towards the centre of the Galaxy: the Sagittarius Arm, one of the Galaxy's dominant features. In this crowded sky you see glowing nebulae, which we call, for their shapes, the Eagle, the Omega, the Trifid, the Lagoon: a huge region of star-birth, one of the largest in the Galaxy, immense clouds of gas and dust each capable of producing millions of stars each.

The Lagoon Nebula, for example, is five thousand light years from Earth. You see a roughly spherical glow illuminated by a clutch of stars at the centre. The embedded stars' light makes the gases shine, out as far as it can reach, before it gets absorbed. But the true nebula is a dark cloud of dust and hydrogen eclipsing the stars behind it, probably containing proto-stars that have yet to shine.

After travelling tens of thousand of light years, after passing through more veils of stars and dust, you begin to approach the Galaxy's centre. The sky here is crowded with stars and glowing dust clouds. The stars seem small, uniform, few of them bright and blue and young, for the stars are deprived of fuel, here in this crammed space. The dust clouds are disrupted, torn into ragged sheets and filaments by the immense forces that operate here.

Towards the heart of the Galaxy itself, there is structure, remnants of ancient events of unimaginable violence. Laced across a backdrop of star swarms you make out two loose rings of light, roughly concentric. The rings are full of detail: clouds of gas and dust, and stars gathered into small, compact globular clusters, spherical knots of all-but-identical pinpoint lights. In one place the outer ring has erupted into a vast knot of star formation, tens of thousands of hot young blue stars blaring from the ragged heart of a pink-white cloud.

The big rings are like expanding ripples, or billows of gas blown out from some explosion. But that must have been immense indeed; that outermost ring is a coherent structure a thousand light years across, big enough to contain almost all the stars visible with the naked eye from Earth.

The inner ring is actually the base of an even larger structure that rises up and out of the general plane of the Galaxy. It is a ragged arch, traced out by filaments of shining gas, arching high into the less crowded sky above. It looks a little like a solar flare, curving gusts of gas shaped by the sun's magnetic field – but this, of course, is immeasurably vaster.

And rising out of the arch you glimpse more immensity still, a vast jet of gas that thrusts out of the Galaxy's plane, glimmering across thousands of light years before dissipating into the dark. It is a hierarchy of enormity, endless expansions of scale up into the dark.

But of the Galaxy centre itself, you can see only a tight, impenetrable cluster of stars, many thousands of them, swarming impossibly close together, closer to each other than the planets of the Solar System. To see the deeper structure you must travel further still, into the crowd of acolyte stars.

At last you reach the heart of the Galaxy. You are within the great central cluster of stars, no more than a couple of dozen light years from the very centre. And at that centre there is a cavity some twenty light years wide, encased by a shell of crowded, disrupted stars.

Here you find a great double-spiral architecture of stars, perhaps as many as two or three million of them, like a miniature copy of the Galaxy trapped here at its heart. The spiralling stars are dragged into their tight orbits around the object at the Galaxy's gravitational core: a black hole with a broad, glowing, spitting accretion disc of infalling matter. The hole itself has the mass of some three million suns. And it is the violent wind from the vast accretion disc, matter crushed by the hole's gravity, which has created this relative hollowness.

But the emptiness of the 'cavity' is only relative. The space here is crammed with gas and dust, its particles ionised and driven to high speeds by the ferocious gravitational and magnetic forces working here, so that streamers of glowing gas criss-cross the cavity in a fine tracery. Stars are still being born here, notably a cluster of blue-hot young stars just a fraction away from the black hole itself. And here and there rogue stars fall through the cavity, and drag streaming trails behind them, glowing brilliantly.

At the centre of our Galaxy stars fall like comets, with tails a hundred light years long.

Our generation is the first to be able to imagine, in such detail, such a remarkable odyssey. But a Galaxy-centre journey, *even at the speed of light*, would take some twenty-five thousand years – five times as long as all human recorded history to date. Alpha Centauri, however, a mere four light years away, will surely be our first destination beyond the sun's empire: a magnificent launching pad for our future among the stars.

But how are we to reach it?

Chapter 18

Stellar Argosies

For I dipt into the future, far as human eye could see,
Saw the Vision of the world, and all the wonder that
    would be;
Saw the heavens fill with commerce, argosies of magic
    sails,
Pilots of the purple twilight, dropping down with costly
    bales . .

— Alfred, Lord Tennyson

The ship loops through an elliptical, two-hour orbit around the
Moon. On the lunar surface, the lights of colonies and mines
glitter.

The ship is a stack of components fifty metres long. At its base is
a massive, reinforced pusher plate, mounted on a shock-absorbing
mechanism of springs and crushable aluminium posts. The main
body of the craft is a cluster of fuel magazines. Big superconducting
hoops encircle the whole stack.

Now pellets of helium-3 and deuterium, mined from lunar soil, are
fired out of the back of the craft, behind the pusher plate. They form
a target the size of a full stop. A bank of carbon dioxide lasers fires
converging beams at the target.

There is a fusion pulse, lasting two hundred and fifty nanoseconds.
And then another, and another.

Three hundred micro-explosions each second hurl energy
against the pusher plate. Slowly, ponderously, the craft is driven
forward. From Earth, the new Moon is made brilliant by fusion
fire.

The ship is fantastically ugly, ungainly. But it is humanity's first starship.

The difficulty with interstellar travel is that the stars are so distant.

The nearest known star is the feeble dwarf Proxima Centauri, some 4.27 light years away – around forty million *million* kilometres. It is all but impossible to grasp these immense distances. If the sun were shrunk to the size of a grain of sand, Earth would orbit just a few centimetres from it, and even remote Pluto would be no more than sixty centimetres out. But Proxima Centauri would be *three kilometres* away.

The universe is a vast and empty space, the stars no more than scattered dust grains. Humans have actually launched four interstellar craft, of a sort: the unmanned Pioneer and Voyager probes of the 1970s. These escaped from the Solar System after slingshotting off the gravity wells of the giant planets. None of them is heading for Proxima, but Voyager 2 will pass within a light year of the nine-light-year-distant star Sirius – in 385,000 years' time.

Our modern rocket technology is just too feeble to challenge such huge distances. How can we do better?

We can certainly think of better ways to build rockets, moving beyond the century-old chemical-engineering technology of our modern ships.

Isaac Newton understood that to make any rocket work, you have to throw something out the back – the faster the better. A continuous nuclear fusion drive would throw out its exhaust a lot faster than our best chemical combustion chamber. But we have come nowhere near to sustaining a fusion reaction for long enough to build a practical starship. A craft driven by photon propulsion would use the ultimate exhaust with the highest possible velocity – particles of light. But the power plant weight and energy you would need to get a practical thrust are staggering.

The craft I sketched at the opening of this chapter is driven by a more practical technology called 'nuclear pulse propulsion'. The ship is driven forward by a series of micro-explosions – fusion of deuterium and helium-3 probably – set off behind a pusher plate. It is like putting a firecracker under a tin can: not pretty, but effective. This concept has actually been proved under the aegis of the United States Air Force, who ran a couple of test flights in 1959 and 1960 with conventional explosives; it was called, a little unkindly, Project Put-Put.

But the enormous distances even to the nearest stars would require an immense amount of fuel, even if the most efficient energy source known – anti-matter annihilating with matter – could be used. Wouldn't it be better if you didn't have to carry any fuel at all?

In 1960 an engineer called Robert Bussard, based at the Los Alamos Scientific Laboratory, came up with a design that appeared to achieve just that.

Space isn't empty. Between the stars there are tenuous clouds of gas: mostly hydrogen, it is the interstellar medium, the stuff of which new stars are made. Bussard proposed drawing in this gas, concentrating it, and pushing it into a fusion reaction, just as hydrogen is burned into helium at the heart of the sun. This design became known as an interstellar ramjet.

The trouble is, the interstellar medium is *so* thin your inlet scoop has to be much wider than the few metres of an air-breathing jet – *much* wider. Bussard proposed using magnetic fields to pull in gas from an immense volume, hundreds of thousands of kilometres across. The interstellar gas would have to be electrically charged first, to be deflected by the magnetic scoops. So you would pepper it with laser beams to heat it to a plasma, as hot as the surface of the sun.

Unfortunately a flaw soon turned up in Bussard's design. Only a hundredth of all that incoming fuel could actually be used as fuel. The rest would pile up before the accelerating craft, clogging its magnetic intakes; Bussard's beautiful ship would expend so much energy pushing through this logjam it could never achieve the kind of speeds essential for interstellar flight.

But there have been various developments of the basic proposal to get around this limitation. The most promising is called RAIR – pronounced 'rare' – for Ram-Augmented Interstellar Rocket. Here, the intake of interstellar hydrogen would be greatly reduced, and would be used only to top up a store the starship was already carrying. There would be two exhausts to push the ship forward: one from the fusion engine, and the other from superheated interstellar gas squirted out of the ship by fusion heat. Nothing resembling a prototype of such a craft has ever been built, of course (not by human engineers, anyhow). But it is thought that the RAIR design could perform two or three times better than the basic Bussard system, and perhaps achieve ten or twenty per cent of the speed of light.

At such speeds, however, it would still take decades to reach even the nearest star. And even if more powerful drives become available we will soon come up against the restriction of the lightspeed barrier.

According to Albert Einstein, nothing moving through space-time can exceed the speed of light. Not only that, it would take an immense amount of effort even to approach that speed (an infinite amount, in Einsteinian theory, to get there). It would thus take *at least* four years to get to Proxima, and because most of the energy expended is eaten up by the last few per cent of velocity, almost certainly it would take a lot longer in practice. By comparison, at present we can't run Earth-orbit space missions of more than a few months without resupply.

The first manned starship might be an artificial habitat, perhaps a huge, rotating cylinder. It will be a one-way trip; indeed generations of humans may live out their lives in space, running a miniature, self-sufficient ecology inside the ship, before making starfall.

All this just to reach the nearest star systems! The thousand-light-year geography of the Galaxy at large appears forever out of reach.

Can we do better still?

It turns out that, in theory at least, it may be possible, if not to beat the light barrier, at least to match it. This can be achieved using a technology familiar to all viewers of television science fiction, and to readers for decades before: teleportation.

The concept behind teleportation – beaming – is simple enough.

You step into some kind of transmitting booth. The booth makes a record of your body: a record complete enough to *reconstruct* your body, atom by atom, neurone by neurone. That record is sent by radio transmission to a remote receiver, where the specification contained in the signal is used to rebuild your body – and, presumably, *you*.

The signal would travel at lightspeed, so it would still take four years to get to Alpha Centauri this way. But to *you*, no time at all would appear to have passed, for during the transmission 'you' would have existed as no more than a pattern of data, crossing from star to star.

We have grown used to the idea of teleportation as a way of hopping from place to place on a planet, or even moving from an orbiting starship to the surface of a planet. But if you have a teleport, why bother with the cost and difficulty of a starship at all? The transmission of signals, even from star to star, presents no difficulties; we can imagine error-correcting codes built into each transmission to ensure fidelity of arbitrarily good accuracy.

But the encoding required to create the signal in the first place is rather more difficult.

We used to think teleportation was impossible, in fact, because you'd need to map the position and velocity of *every* particle making up your body. And that violates the Uncertainty Principle of quantum mechanics, which states that there is a fundamental fuzziness to reality, making it impossible to determine *both* the position and velocity of any particle at the same time.

But it may be that there is a way around the Uncertainty Principle. Quantum mechanics allows for the long-range correlation of particles. Once they've been in contact, they're never truly separated, their future evolution commingled. This is called 'Einstein-Podolsky-Rosen (EPR) correlation'.

To build a teleport link, you must send the receiving gate to its destination by some conventional means, a slower-than-light ship. The gate is EPR-correlated with a transmitter back home. The transmitter makes a joint measurement on itself and the quantum properties of the object to be teleported. The transmitter sends the receiver gate the result of the measurement. Knowing this, the receiver can convert some of its correlated material into an exact replica of the unknown quantum state the transmitter measured. In essence you have sent across information about the quantum state of your transmitted object.

This is all rather technical, and relies on somewhat eerie properties of the quantum world which – though real and measurable – few people are comfortable with. But it does allow, in principle, a way for teleportation to be achieved, and the concept appears to have been proved by researchers who claim to have 'teleported' a single photon.

There are many practical difficulties to be addressed in all this. You are rather more than an elemental object like a photon; your body contains some ten billion billion *billion* atoms. And therefore it would take the same number of kilobytes, to order of magnitude, to store the data encoding its structure. By comparison, all the books ever written probably amount to a mere thousand billion kilobytes: the data compression required would be spectacular, to say the least.

And the Uncertainty Principle still has a sting in its tail.

You can't clone quantum information. You can swap it around, but you can't copy it, as you can everyday information. The teleporter has to *destroy* the object it's going to teleport – that is, you. And, of course, there's no guarantee of reconstruction.

If you feel uneasy about the notion of walking into a booth that will destroy you, even on the promise of reconstruction at some wonderful destination – well, you will gain sympathy from the ghosts of many philosophers of the past. There is much we have yet to learn about the nature of human consciousness, and teleportation draws us into the ancient debate over dualism. Do 'you' exist independently of your body, or are 'you' simply a pattern emergent from your body? Would that reconstructed heap of atoms at Proxima Centauri, however perfect a copy, even if it walked and talked like you, actually *be* you? (Not surprisingly this issue is never touched on in the TV shows!)

Still, if the physical and philosophical difficulties can be overcome, a teleport interstellar transportation system would make sense on one level: economic sense. The cost of information transfer is at least a billion times less than the cost of the equivalent physical transfer, by means of a ship hauling your flesh and blood between the stars.

Even with a teleporter, however, if I were to complete a round trip to the centre of the Galaxy and back, I would find that fifty thousand years had elapsed before my return.

With such delays, it is hard to imagine that with signalling and any physical transfer restricted to lightspeed, that any coherent inter-stellar society could be built. We may forever find ourselves inhabiting scattered islands, separated from home and our neigh-bours by decades of travel – unless there is a way around Einstein's lightspeed dictum after all.

And perhaps even that is possible.

The way to break Einstein's speed-of-light law is to look at the small print. You can't travel faster than light going *through* space-time . . . so what you must do is to go *around* space-time, or take it with you.

The idea of the 'space-time wormhole', a short cut through space, has also become familiar to us through science fiction shows. Einstein himself taught us that space-time is malleable. You always measure the speed of light in a vacuum at a constant value, no matter how fast you travel yourself, because space and time themselves adjust to make it so (distorting your clocks and measuring rods as you travel): you bend space and time, just a little, every time you take a walk.

The idea of a wormhole is to bend space-time so severely that two points which are far apart are drawn together and could be connected by a wormhole, a short tunnel. It would then be possible to cover immense distances *without* violating light-speed, by popping through the wormhole short cut.

Surprisingly the idea has a (reasonably!) firm theoretical footing. The astronomer Carl Sagan, wanting to use the idea in his 1980 novel *Contact*, asked physicist Kip Thorne to put some theoretical flesh on the notion. Thorne found, to his surprise, that the concept made sense.

•

Another intriguing possibility is 'space-time surfing'. A physicist called Miguel Alcubierre, working at the University of Wales, has shown it may be possible to create *waves* of space-time. Because these waves are made *of* space-time they do not travel *through* space-time . . . and so aren't subject to the lightspeed law. A spacecraft could 'surf' such a wave, and be carried at arbitrarily high speeds. Surfing would have the advantage that you could go anywhere you liked. Wormholes, by comparison, connect two fixed points.

'Quantum tunnelling' is a rather more subtle approach. According to quantum mechanics particles like electrons are not simple pellets with definite positions and speeds, but ghostly entities described by probabilities. You can never be sure where a given electron is or where it is heading. So if you try to contain an electron by an energy barrier, there is a small but finite probability – because of the Uncertainty Principle – that you'll suddenly find it on the far side of the barrier. And if you do, there is no appreciable delay . . .

We don't yet know if any of these faster-than-light methods are possible even in theory – wormholes, for instance, seem to require a new form of mass-energy called 'negative energy' to be kept open – but on the other hand no one has yet shown they are impossible. And what isn't impossible is only a matter of engineering.

But if *we* can imagine ways to beat the distances to the stars, couldn't others?

Chapter 19

Strangers in a Strange Land

Where did you come from, baby dear?
Out of the everywhere into here.

— **George MacDonald**

There are those who believe that the stars have been crossed already: that aliens have visited the Earth, and may indeed be among us now. There are even some who believe they have made personal contact with these visitors.

Personally I am sceptical. But in arguing against the alien-contact interpretation of the UFO phenomenon, I do believe it is important to be open-minded. It is not enough, for example, to argue that interstellar travel is impossible, that the stars are just too far away. It is true that the stars are out of our reach for now. But we have already seen that they could in principle be reached by a civilisation of sufficient power – our own, or another.

In considering UFO claims, we have to question what on Earth (literally!) these UFOnauts are doing here – and the motivation of interstellar visitors is a key subject for later chapters.

But there are separate objections concerning the details of observations claimed of UFOs. The classic morphology of UFOs – disc shapes, for instance – appears to make no sense for a craft that has to manoeuvre in an atmosphere. What about aerodynamics? What about streamlining?

And then you have the spectacular UFO aerobatics reported by many observers. Such gigantic accelerations would surely destroy any conceivable life forms aboard.

So UFOs – whatever their origin, whatever their psychological importance to us, whatever the motives of their putative crews – just couldn't work as engineering . . . Could they? Can we see how it would be possible, even given what we know now, to build a star-travelling UFO to the classic specification?

The answer, surprisingly, is 'maybe'.

How could a 'saucer' shape fly in the atmosphere?

At the Rensselaer Institute in New York, futuristic experiments are going on into technologies which would make it possible for *any* shape of craft to fly – a saucer, even a brick – regardless of the rules of traditional aircraft design. And in some respects a saucer shape may even be the best.

The secret is an 'air spike', a laser beam or focused microwave beam fitted to the front of a craft which carves a path through the air. The airflow around a craft could be controlled even at many times the speed of sound, and the craft would suffer little drag, significantly improving its performance.

A craft guided by an air spike could be so light it could fly without a power plant, taking its energy from lasers or microwave beams transmitted from satellites. The engineers at Rensselaer imagine a 'lightcraft', a flying saucer ten metres across which would propel itself behind an air spike by using magnetic fields at its rim to push charged air backwards.

And why a flying saucer shape? To give a large surface area, to catch all those beamed-down microwaves . . .

Right now the air spike has only been tested in wind tunnels, and there are many practical problems – not least the tendency of detonations of exploding air to travel up the spike and destroy the craft – but NASA is considering investing in the technology. And experiments are continuing to take the concept up to Mach Twenty-five, fast enough to reach orbit.

But even an air spike may not be enough. The accelerations and manoeuvrability imputed to UFOs by some observers seem to transcend the boundaries of current technological thinking. Surely to achieve such a startling performance without turning the crew into strawberry jam would require control at a deeper level . . . perhaps control over inertia.

But that's impossible, isn't it? Once again, there may be loopholes in the laws of physics.

Inertia is the awkward property of mass that it takes energy to get it moving, and to stop it again. If inertia could be diminished or removed, a thousand-tonne spacecraft could be set in motion at enormous speeds with no more force than a puff of air.

Three physicists called Haisch, Rueda and Puthoff are studying the causes of inertia itself.

The 'empty' vacuum is not empty at all, but a wash of seething energy, with 'virtual' particles popping in and out of existence constantly. This so-called 'zero point field' creates an electromagnetic drag on any object which passes through it. And it is that drag which, according to Haisch, Rueda and Puthoff, *creates* the effect of inertia.

If this effect could be adjusted and controlled, then a craft could be rendered virtually massless by inertial suppressors, and so capable of being driven to enormous velocities by a very modest push indeed.

Imagine an interstellar spacecraft, then: capable of travelling between stars in a matter of days or weeks by quantum tunnelling or traversing wormholes; manoeuvrable in the air thanks to something like an air spike; its crew protected from crushing accelerations by dampened inertia . . .

Such a craft *could* form the small, compact scout ship of UFO legend.

All of this is speculative, of course. But I do feel we should keep open minds as to the technological capabilities of advanced civilisations. If *we* can think up such notions, what might 'they' be capable of?

Personally I would need very hard evidence to convince me of the reality of alien contact. While the technology reported in UFO sightings may (just!) be plausible, I find it very hard to believe that creatures advanced enough to cross the stars would behave in the secretive, vindictive and downright irrational manner the reports claim.

But what about our behaviour?

Suppose the aliens stopped messing about and showed themselves. Imagine incontrovertible proof: the saucer landing on the White House lawn, or even a crashed starship in the fields of southern England. How would we react?

First contact with aliens is a marvellous dream. We imagine, as in Carl Sagan's *Contact*, receiving wisdom from the stars: an *Encyclopaedia Galactica*, a cultural adrenalin boost that will raise our society to new levels. Or perhaps we will come across a wonderful alien artefact – an abandoned city on Mars, a crashed ship on the Moon – and by unlocking its secrets we will accelerate our technological understanding by generations.

But would it really be like that? Historically most technological and cultural advances have been ruthlessly exploited for profit, power and weapons potential. Why would our reaction to an alien discovery be any different?

Perhaps this question can't be answered until the contact happens. But there is a precedent from history.

In September 1851 Captain Robert M'Clure was guiding a British exploration ship, HMS *Investigator*, along the north coast of Banks Island in the Arctic. Towards the island's eastern cape M'Clure found a shallow, protected embayment, which he called the Bay of God's Mercy. He and his men wintered there. The following summer the ice did not clear from the bay, and they were forced to overwinter again.

In the spring of 1853 the crew was reached by a rescue party from a sister ship, HMS *Resolute*. M'Clure reluctantly abandoned the *Investigator* and followed the rescue party back to Melville Island.

A group of Eskimos living three hundred kilometres away on Victoria Island somehow heard about the abandoned ship. These Kanghiryuakmiut and Kanghiryuachiakmiut people, living largely by seal hunting, had never seen Europeans. Indeed they would not be contacted by whites until American whalers visited them in 1906, when they would be christened the 'Copper Eskimos' for the tools they made from local copper deposits.

These people made their way to Mercy Bay.

Imagine how this must have been for the Copper Eskimos. The *Investigator* was a 450-tonne copper-sheathed vessel, thoroughly modern for its time. To the Eskimos it must indeed have seemed like a crashed starship, its origin inexplicable, full of wonders.

How did the Copper Eskimos react? Did they seek out cultural artefacts, study books and maps and instruments, try to understand the strange beings who had inhabited this ship, seek to emulate their superior technologies?

Not a bit of it.

The Copper Eskimos were not wealthy, even in their own terms. They lived at the wrong end of two long Arctic trade routes, from Siberia and the interior of Canada. They had only seal skins to trade for the materials they needed to survive. Now, thanks to the *Investigator*'s unimaginably precious raw materials, they would be able to reverse the flow of trade goods. In the fragile economy of the Arctic peoples, the *Investigator* would make the Copper Eskimos rich.

The Eskimos began annual summer migrations north across the ice to Mercy Bay. They mined the ship, and its crew's caches on land. They salvaged strips of iron and sheets of canvas, softwood boards, copper sheathing, woven cloth, hemp lines, wool yarn, and leather. Then, each autumn, when the first snows provided a travelling surface for the sleds, the Copper Eskimos would return south to their home country, where seal hunting kept them in good stead through the winter. The next year they would return, using the same hunting sites.

They kept their sleds and dog panniers light, carrying little food from their winter bases, to leave room for salvage. So, during each summer, while they scavenged the ship as a base, they had to live off the land. Using the ship's metals they systematically hunted the local fauna, such as moulting geese (which, flightless, could not escape), fish – and a great many musk oxen.

Within a few decades the local musk oxen population was wiped out.

By 1890, nobody travelled to the *Investigator* any more, even though there were still valuables to salvage, because there were no more musk oxen left to kill. The ship itself sank or floated away. No musk oxen was seen on the island until 1952, after which the population began to recover.

To tell this story is not to judge the actions of people surviving in the harshest of environments. The Copper Eskimos' first priority could not be cultural contact; it had to be food, raw materials, and a way to buy the goods they needed.

Nevertheless the Eskimos seem to have shown absolutely no curiosity about the remarkable ship, how it had fallen to earth amongst them, or the people who had manned it. All that mattered was the wealth the ship contained.

We like to believe that we are more advanced than that: rational, scientific, open to new phenomena and cultures – and, besides, with our full bellies, we have the leisure and energy for curiosity. But if the Starship *Enterprise* were to plummet to Earth in New Jersey or Sussex or Tuscany, would we really be so different from the Copper Eskimos?

We can't know what an alien culture would bring to an encounter with us. But we already suspect, sadly, what we would bring: nothing but our flawed humanity.

Chapter 20

Galaxy for Sale

> Alexander wept when he heard from Anaxarchus that
> there was an infinite number of worlds . . . 'Do you not
> think it lamentable that with such a vast multitude of
> worlds, we have not yet conquered one?'
>
> — **Plutarch**

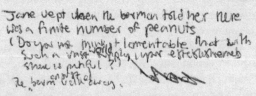

If we succeed in building starships, what shall we do with them?
How about colonising the Galaxy?

The physicist Frank Tipler has proposed a way we humans could
colonise, not just nearby stars, but the Galaxy – and cheaply into the
bargain.

Tipler's scheme assumes nothing much beyond the slower-than-
light transport methods we can easily envisage today. Just as in our
exploration of the Solar System, we will begin with unmanned
probes. The first wave will be slow, no faster than we can afford.

The probes will be self-replicating: capable of constructing anything, given raw materials, including copies of themselves. The
physicist John von Neumann has shown that such machines are
possible, and, after all, human beings are capable of replication with
very little training . . .

When a ship arrives at its target, its crew, of robots or humans, will
found a colony. They will surely be able to populate their new system
rapidly – say within a few centuries, the time it took to build modern

America from scratch – and then it will be time for a new generation to build more ships and move on, further and deeper into the Galaxy, in search of homes of their own.

The average rate of expansion will surely be slow, much slower than the speed of light. However fast the great interstellar transports, the migrants will need time to form their colonies and establish themselves before building new starships to continue the onward push. And as time goes on we can't expect a simple diffusion outwards; the growing colonies are going to interact – we'll see empires, even wars – and the friction will slow down the rate of expansion.

But we can expect the migration to continue, in all directions outward from the Earth, pretty relentlessly once it has started.

And, once started, the process is self-directing, even self-financing, because the new colonies will be built of local resources, requiring nothing of Earth. *We* must invest merely in the cost of the initial generation of probes. Thus, the cost of colonising the Galaxy would be less, in real terms, than that of the Apollo programme of the 1960s – a key part of Tipler's argument that all this is feasible and, indeed, quite likely.

How long will it take to cover the Galaxy?

Now, the Galaxy is indeed a big place, a hundred thousand light years across. Even if the colonising wave front moves, on average, at lightspeed, it would take a hundred thousand years to cover the Galaxy. If the front moves at a much more conservative one hundredth of lightspeed, the Galaxy would be covered in ten million years.

Ten million years – an immense period of time, of course, in human terms. But the Galaxy is perhaps a *thousand* times older than this. There will be time enough for us to build our empire.

But we must be careful we do not burn ourselves up first, for hidden in Tipler's scenarios are dread warnings for our future.

We saw in earlier chapters that growth – exponential growth – is relentless. If we maintain our historic population growth rates, we could cover the Solar System in a few centuries or millennia. And even if we go on to the stars in this fashion, the deadly logic of the numbers will pursue us.

As to what happens after that, the lessons of our history to date are not encouraging.

The story of the Polynesians is perhaps our nearest analogue to interstellar colonisation. The Polynesians spread out among their islands for over a thousand years, across three thousand kilometres, right through a triangle of the Pacific based on Easter Island, New Zealand and Hawaii.

They didn't have compasses or writing or metals tools, but they made terrific sailing canoes and could navigate wonderfully. And this was no chance wandering; they carried with them crops and livestock, bananas and pigs and chickens. They knew what they were doing: they meant to colonise.

But by about AD 1000 the colonisation wave front had reached as far as it could go, and the Polynesians had inhabited every scrap of land. Isolated, surrounded by islands full of people, they fell on themselves.

Consider Easter Island. The colonists' descendants destroyed the native ecosystem in a few generations, let the soil erode away, and, by cutting and burning, they wiped out the forests, so they couldn't even build any more canoes.

Without wood for boats or houses, they had to abandon the sea, along with any hope of escape or trade. And with the soil vanishing, the animals and birds eaten, they couldn't even feed themselves. What was left was native rock, from which they carved their haunting, desolate sculptures. But their political structures were overturned by military leaders, and civil war spread as they fought over the remaining cultivable land.

At last they turned to cannibalism. By the time the Europeans arrived the islanders had just about wiped themselves out.

It was the same story all over the Polynesian triangle. In some cases the islanders died out altogether.

There was an island called Henderson, for instance, close to

Pitcairn. It was remote and marginal – a coral reef, thrust above the water by a geologic uplift, so it had no basalt or other rocks to make tools. It didn't even have reliable fresh water, because the rain leaked away through the porous limestone. But a small number of people survived here, for centuries. They lived on trade with the neighbouring islands, exchanging coral and sea produce like shellfish and turtle eggs for tools of volcanic stone and glass.

The trade fell apart when the other islands' ecosystems crashed, and the canoes stopped coming. The stone tools broke; the oven stones shattered. The native trees weren't big enough for the islanders to make ships of their own. Stranded, they confronted an insoluable problem: how to survive on an island with no tools or even stone except limestone.

They tried. They used shells and bird bones to make tools. They used coral and clamshell for oven stones. They made fish hooks as best they could from purse shells. But it wasn't sustainable. They lasted a century or so with these pathetic tools, their numbers dwindling.

It is a chill thought that there must have been a last Henderson islander of all. How did he or she die? Alone, in bed? At the coast, peering out for the canoes which would never come again?

Could this be the bleak pattern of our future?

Suppose we start colonising the stars, after the manner of Tipler, or otherwise. Suppose there's no limit on the ships we can build, the people we can carry; the only limit is the number of stars we can reach, the planets and other resources we can find.

Earth is suddenly the centre of a growing sphere of colonisation, a sphere whose volume has to keep increasing to keep up with the population growth. The leading edge, the colonising wave, has to sweep on faster and faster, eating up worlds and stars and moving on to the next, because of the pressure from behind . . . But at a (compound) growth rate of just a few per cent, *that leading edge would be moving at lightspeed within a few centuries*.

A crowded system within the colonisation sphere, running out of resources, will find itself surrounded by systems just as heavily populated, and as heavily armed, as it is – and nobody can escape. It is a recipe for disaster, indeed for war.

The universe is a place of limits, of cruel equations. We *must* eventually learn to contain our growth, because exponential growth *must* overwhelm any resource pool, sooner or later; and when we grow so fast that we are spreading out at lightspeed (still the best bet for the universal speed limit) we will begin to starve.

It would be nice to imagine that the starfarers of the future will be rather smarter than the Polynesians about managing their resources, and their own numbers. But remember that the logic of exponential growth predicts a rapid spread. Those hungry, desperate starfarers, fleeing at lightspeed, might be little further removed in time from *us* than we are from the Polynesians.

Let us continue to be optimistic; let us suppose we avoid the Polynesian trap. Consider the Galaxy ten million years hence. (To put that in perspective, ten million years in the past our ancestors had not yet split off from the line that would lead to the chimps and gorillas.)

In this distant future, the Tiplerian logic has worked itself out. The whole Galaxy is populated, from rim to core, by human beings.

This colonisation is quite obvious as we look up into the night sky. We see belts and rings encircling each planet. We see spheres enclosing whole stars, trapping and exploiting all their output of heat and light. We see stars and worlds arranged to suit the needs of mankind: a whole ring of worlds in the orbit of Earth, for instance. We could even imagine a huge lens-shaped surface enclosing the entire Galaxy.

Like ants crawling around the rim of a swimming pool, we may not understand everything we see, but we will surely be unable to miss the work of human hands.

But the people of this age are difficult for us to understand. They may retain the ancient human form; but if they do it will be for sentimental reasons only. Perhaps they have evolved some more useful form, such as that of a bush robot: a mechanical form shaped like a tree, with a series of branching limbs, going all the way down to the microscopic. Most humans are probably adapted to living in open space, away from the planets, and feeding directly from starlight, because that way the Galaxy is able to support a much greater population. Life is three-dimensional. It is as if we have returned to an ocean: a new ocean, the ocean of space.

This may be the peak of human fortunes, 'the manhood of the race', as H. G. Wells put it. But we aren't at home here. We are primitives, and the human descendants of the future are all but incomprehensible to us; and there is nobody like us left alive.

. . . But in this wonderful, or terrifying, vision there is a mystery.

Nice way to
end a chapter.

Chapter 21

Innumerable Earths

Innumerable suns exist; innumerable Earths revolve around these suns in a manner similar to the way the seven planets revolve around our sun. Living beings inhabit these worlds . . .

— **Giordano Bruno**

Today, polls indicate that many modern humans, at least in the educated world, have a deep intuition that life on Earth cannot be unique.

This makes sense, as a glance at the sky demonstrates. We know that the sun is a star; it appears larger and brighter than the rest only because it is closer. Conversely, if the other stars are suns, then we understand they must be very far away. We are surrounded by immensities on all sides.

Earth is just a speck in all that vastness. There *must* be life out there. Mustn't there?

So far we have found no evidence of life beyond Earth, but it isn't for lack of trying. Systematic searches of the sky have been underway for decades, without success.

With our great radio telescopes we could detect a civilisation as powerful as ourselves anywhere within a few thousand light years of Earth. We haven't.

There is a classification of possible civilisations that includes a Type

K1 – a level we are approaching, able to manipulate matter and energy on a planetary scale – and K2, which has mastered the power of a star. We could detect a true K1 across forty thousand light years, from beyond the centre of the Galaxy. We haven't.

A K2 would blare as bright as a star on radio wavelengths. It wouldn't be a question of the astronomers of Carl Sagan's *Contact* and their endless search for scratchy radio whispers from the stars: a K2 would be unmissable, *even from a neighbouring galaxy*. We don't hear any.

What's more, we don't *see* the aliens.

There is no convincing evidence that they have been here, at any time in the past. The Solar System appears to be primordial, in the sense that it shows no signs of great engineering projects we can already envisage, such as the terraforming of Mars or Venus. The Moon appears ancient and unmodified.

We don't see any signs that they have been here on Earth either. It isn't simply the lack of high-tech artefacts in the archaeological layers, or cave paintings of men in bubble helmets: the evolution of life on Earth itself appears unmodified. For life's first two billion years on Earth, it was stuck at the level of single cells. A single sneeze from an alien astronaut from some higher-evolved biosphere would surely have changed the course of life on Earth, and maybe even wiped out the native life. But that didn't happen; there can have been no such sneeze.

There is a further hierarchy of hypothetical civilisations above the K1 and K2 levels. A Type K3 civilisation would manipulate the mass-energy of a galaxy; and so on. Perhaps a Type Omega civilisation, encompassing the universe, would be able to shape the evolution of the cosmos, perform such miracles as time travel, even change the constants of physics.

A Type Omega, admittedly, might be hard for us to recognise! But we ought to be able to see a Type K3, even in a neighbouring galaxy. Imagine a galaxy with all the stars farmed: covered by sunlight-trapping spheres, or their physics altered, perhaps to extend their lifetimes. Imagine the whole of a galaxy enclosed by an energy-capturing structure.

Even if we didn't understand, even if we had no idea what such great structures are for, surely we would recognise them as artificial. Even if the builders are long gone, surely we should see their mighty ruins all around us.

But we see none of this. Nothing at all. We seem to be surrounded by a *Great Silence*.

It just doesn't feel right.

Life on other worlds is actually a very old hypothesis.

In 300 BC Epicurus proposed that if atoms were infinite in number then 'there are infinite worlds both like and unlike this world'. The Roman Lucretius argued that if the seeds of life filled a huge universe 'it is in the highest degree unlikely that this Earth and sky is the only one to have been created'.

These ideas were eclipsed by Aristotle and the early Christians, who put forward a universe with Earth at the centre, and therefore unique. But the Copernican revolution of four centuries ago demolished this argument, and the Earth came to be seen once more as not a special place – and therefore life elsewhere seemed likely.

A key support of the early arguments for extraterrestrial life was Galileo's first telescopic observation of the moons of Jupiter, like a miniature Solar System in its own right. As Kepler observed, 'Those four little moons exist for Jupiter, not for us . . . We deduce with the highest degree of probability that Jupiter is inhabited.'

The cleric Giordano Bruno, quoted at the opening of this chapter, lived in the sixteenth century. Bruno was the first thinker to have expressed something like the modern notion of a plurality of worlds – of planets orbiting suns, many of them inhabited by beings more or less like humans. (Earlier thinkers on other worlds had imagined parallel versions of an Aristotlean pocket universe, centred on a stationary Earth.) Bruno, incidentally, was burned by the Church in 1600, though for a mystical attack on Christianity, not for his argument about aliens.

This powerful intuition of the commonness of life has always caused great controversy, just as it does today. Saint Augustine, for example, decided aliens couldn't exist. If they did, they would require salvation – a Christ of their own – but that would remove the uniqueness of Christ, which is impossible, theologically speaking.

But today we can put our (perfectly good) intuition about the prevalence of life beyond Earth on a firmer footing.

The scientists used to think that life was pretty unlikely – maybe even unique to Earth. Astronomer Fred Hoyle once remarked that the idea that you could shuffle organic molecules in some primaeval soup and, purely by chance, come up with something as exquisite and complex as a DNA molecule is like watching a whirlwind pass through an aircraft factory and assemble the scattered parts into a Boeing 747.

But now we think such notions are wrong. Now we think that the complexity that defines and underlies life is somehow hardwired into the laws of physics. It is *emergent*.

Imagine boiling a pan of water. As the liquid starts to convect, you'll see a regular pattern of cells form, like a honeycomb, just before the proper boiling cuts in and the motion becomes chaotic. Now, all there is in the pan is water molecules, billions of them. Nobody is *telling* the molecules how to organise themselves into those striking patterns – and yet they organise anyhow. That is a simple example of how order and complexity can emerge from an initial uniform and featureless state.

And maybe life is just the end product of a long series of similar self-organising steps.

However it managed the trick, life on Earth cut in as soon as it could, more than three billion years ago, just about as soon as the rocks had cooled enough for water to gather, it seems.

Our scientific world-view is based on certain fundamental philosophical principles. We believe nature is uniform, so the laws and processes that work here must work everywhere else. We believe in the 'principle of plenitude': that if something is possible in nature, it happens. And we hold to the 'Copernican principle': we believe that we aren't in any unique place in space or time.

So we have come to believe that if life self-started so rapidly here on Earth, it must be emergent *everywhere*.

What's more, our experience of Earth shows us that if life exists it spreads.

We have found life on Earth everywhere we have looked: from the rarefied heights of the atmosphere to the depths of the ocean, in volcanoes, in boiling pools, under the ice, in lakes of soda or acid, in gushers of boiling salt water, feeding off the thin seep of minerals from vents in the oceans' deepest depths. There are even hardy bacteria called 'cryptoendoliths' which have found a way to survive the ferocious environment of Antarctica's dry valleys – drenched by ultraviolet, subject to searing cold, places so dry that stray seals are mummified – by living *inside* rocks.

Life spreads. It does so with or without intelligent direction, for there are sound evolutionary reasons for it to do so. Not only that, we can already think of ways life could spread to the stars.

But if life self-starts everywhere, and it spreads wherever it can, how come we don't have incontrovertible in-your-face proof that extraterrestrial life has spread *here*?

We can already think of ways to reach the stars (see Chapter 18). Surely other races could do the same. So interstellar travel can't be ruled out because it is technologically infeasible.

It may seem that the universe could be teeming with life, but the place is so darned *big* that we are doomed to be forever isolated; it is just too unlikely we would ever get to meet anybody else, even if we were all equipped with interstellar drives, because they are so far away. Is that the reason we see no evidence of aliens among us?

It turns out that with a little thought this objection too can be demolished. Remember (Chapter 20) that Frank Tipler has shown, making no dramatic assumptions about technological leaps, that a species like ourselves could colonise the Galaxy in ten million years.

If *we* can do this, so could somebody else. And the Galaxy is so old that there has been time for a ten-million-year expansion by alien species to have happened before – not just once, but a *thousand times over*.

We ought to see their 'bright boroughs and circle-citadels'; the mark of their civilisation on the Galaxy would be as unmissable as the lights of Los Angeles from the air.

But we don't see them.

Where *is* everybody?

This argument is a development of a back-of-the-envelope calculation first made by the great physicist Enrico Fermi (supposedly in the course of an argumentative lunch). It is the basis of one of the deepest paradoxes facing us today, as we contemplate our existence and the universe around us. It is known as the 'Fermi Paradox', and it is simply stated: The aliens *should* exist, because we think life emerges everywhere. Some of them *should* have spread to the stars by now. We *should* be able to see them, or hear them. But we don't see them; all we have is an absence of evidence.

Something is wrong.

Chapter 22

The Silent Stars

If they existed, they would be here.

— Enrico Fermi

Booby

✓ If we did not exist, we would not
be here.

On a research visit to Houston I was privileged to visit the laboratory where NASA stores its samples of extraterrestrial materials: meteorites, the famous (or infamous) Mars meteorite from Antarctica with its putative traces of ancient life, and most of NASA's Moon rocks, collected by Apollo astronauts.

As I gazed into this gleaming Cold War lab, where the Moon rocks sat like wizened old men in a hospital ward, I wondered if rocks ever shatter under thermal stress, up there on the Moon.

In the deserts of Earth, you see, you can sometimes hear rocks crack in the night. The temperatures, swinging between the heat of the day and the sometimes deep cold of night, puts the rocks under stress; the repeated cycles of expansion and contraction can be enough to shatter them.

A kindly NASA geologist put me right.

On the Moon there are indeed plenty of rocks, and without the shielding of atmosphere there is a much wider temperature swing than on Earth between day and night. You would think those savage stresses would be sufficient to make a rock crack, now and again.

You'd be wrong. The Moon's surface is old, billions of years old, unimaginably old; the Earth, with its geologically recycled surface, is young by comparison. It is hard for us with our mayfly life spans to grasp the meaning of such immense spans of time. But the key apprehension is that every process that *can* occur in such an old, worn-out environment as the Moon's *has* occurred – in fact gone to its limit, until it can operate no more.

Bluntly speaking, there has been time enough for every Moon rock that was likely to crack to have cracked by now. So you won't see rocks shattering on the Moon.

It is the immense age of the Galaxy, and the universe beyond, that gives the Fermi Paradox such power. The universe is old: several times older than the Moon, perhaps *a hundred thousand times* older than the human species. You may think the universe is so big that there could be life swarming out there, but too far away for us to see. But that intuition is wrong. The age factor overcomes the size factor. There has been time for the universe to have been overrun by life, not once but *thousands* of times.

It is as if we found a pristine rock on the Moon, never kissed by the sun, never subject to the Moon's temperature swings, never pocked by a single micrometeorite. It just wouldn't make sense – and nor does Fermi.

Possible resolutions of the Fermi Paradox have been extensively explored in science fiction, and in science.

The simplest possibility of all might be that we just can't see the aliens.

On the fringes of the Galaxy are strange dark objects called MACHOs. We see the way their gravity bends light, but that's all we can see.

Some physicists have proposed that MACHOs may be made of *mirror matter*. The idea of mirror matter, first suggested in the 1980s, is that every particle in nature has an elusive unseen twin, all of it generated in the Big Bang. Mirror matter could clump into stars and planets. But a mirror world would have its own set of physical laws, different to ours. A mirror star would have about half a solar mass – just right to explain the MACHOs – and it would burn faster than our stars, dying young.

Is it possible the MACHOs are mirror stars? Are there planets inhabited by mirror organisms, invisible to our senses? Do ships of mirror matter slide through our Solar System even now, their crews as oblivious to us as we are to them?

This must be one possibility. But the secret of the 'invisibility' of the aliens might lie in us, not them.

We tend to think of our eyes as little cameras, our ears as microphones. They aren't. Sensory information is broken down into shards of perception, which are broken down again to be stored in the brain as memory fragments. And at night, as the body rests, these fragments are brought out from storage, reassembled and replayed.

The brain does not capture a fixed record of events. Instead the brain creates and recreates a picture of the world – neural Chinese whispers. And this recreation is framed by prejudice about what the brain imagines *ought* to be out there.

We seem to be born with habits of thought, knee-jerk reactions, orderings of perception. For example, the very youngest children are fascinated by magic tricks which make objects disappear (try it): on a fundamental level, we arrive in the world already armed with the idea that objects do not simply dematerialise at will.

Limitations of our sensory processing have been harmless, or even beneficial, up to now (if not, they would have been evolved out). But sometimes our perception is faulty. For example, we consistently over-estimate horizontal distance compared to vertical distance. That's why the sky looks like a flattened dome, not a true hemisphere.

And if we aren't programmed to register something, we simply don't see it.

There is an apocryphal story that Captain Cook encountered islanders who seemed unable to see his great ships until the crew launched their boats to row to shore. The islanders had never seen

•
180

such huge structures before, and they simply did not have the conceptual equipment to take them in.

We look out into the night sky and see no signs of life: no whizzing spaceships, no structures among the stars. But we evolved as plains-dwelling hunter-gatherers, and our sensoriums are conditioned to the hundred-kilometre scale of Earth landscapes. Maybe the aliens are indeed all around us, but like Cook's islanders, we just can't see their mighty ships.

A rather more comforting notion is the idea of 'transcendence'.

Perhaps there is some higher form of existence: as unimaginable to us as the pattern on a tapestry to a single thread of its weave, or a Beethoven symphony to a single neurone in its composer's brain. Perhaps sapient life forms find their way to this superior form quite rapidly, and discard such trivialities as radio signals and starships. This kind of possibility has been extensively explored in the fiction of Arthur C. Clarke, for example. If this is true, it must be our duty to find our own way to that better place.

But is it really believable that *all* the other races have become transcendent? Remember, the Galaxy is a big place. All it would take is *one* species of losers or throwbacks at something like our level of achievement to be broadcasting somewhere out there, and we would hear them.

This problem of consistency, it turns out, is a key objection to many proposed Fermi Paradox resolutions. After all we humans, all one species, don't behave the same way; why should a Galaxy full of species that presumably evolved in very different circumstances share the same destiny, or motivations? Whatever mechanism you prefer for destroying or excluding the aliens, remember that all it would take is *one* exception to contradict it.

Another possible resolution to the Fermi Paradox is that few species actually choose to explore and strive for contact as we do: we can imagine a stable, bucolic society, content with their level of achievement, without wishing for further growth.

A somewhat more gloomy possibility is that an advanced enough species may conclude there is nothing worth travelling *for*. Perhaps all conscious experience is in some sense equivalent; what is the use of travelling across the Galaxy if there is nothing new to learn?

Or it may be that there are many species – like the dolphins, perhaps – with intelligence but without the opportunity to make tools, because they live in an aqueous environment, or are spun out among the great rich interstellar clouds . . .

But again, however many thanks-for-the-fish philosophers or bucolic utopians or jaded know-it-alls there are, to resolve Fermi you have to believe that *everybody* is the same; all it would take is *one* exception, one brash, noisy, expansionist species like ourselves, and we would notice them – and remember, being expansionist may be an evolutionary advantage.

Another class of possibilities is that they are indeed out there, *but they choose not to be seen by us*. This kind of notion is generally known as the 'zoo hypothesis'.

This idea has been extensively explored in science fiction. In *Star Trek*, the Prime Directive dictates that junior species should be left alone and given room to grow until they have reached star flight capacity. Perhaps we are being studied, for whatever special features our primitive intelligences display; if we had been overwhelmed by a Galactic civilisation billions of years old, we might never have developed our own distinctive culture, produced our own master-pieces of art and literature, perhaps never even have acquired our own unique insights into science.

Or perhaps we are even being 'farmed' in some way, as in David Brin's *Uplift* novels, in which secretive Galactic races enhance the intelligence of junior species according to a strict and ancient code.

The 'studying' could be somewhat more interactive. Perhaps they are here, all around us, concealed in some kind of duck blinds. The notion that extraterrestrials are in fact working here on Earth, conducting biological experiments on us in league with secretive governments, is of course the cornerstone of modern UFO mythology: the Roswell hypothesis. This seems the depth of paranoia, and it is hard to believe any race advanced enough for star travel would want or need to behave in such a fashion – but it actually fits the facts behind the Fermi Paradox, so must not be too easily dismissed!

Or perhaps we are in quarantine. Perhaps we are being protected from some dread danger Out There; or perhaps *they* are protecting themselves from *us*. In Greg Egan's fine science fiction novel *Quarantine*, we prove capable of destroying whole alien worlds by simply looking at them (through subtle extrapolations of quantum mechanics) – well worth fencing off . . .

But once again, with any such avoidance strategy, there is the problem of consistency. All it would take is *one* rogue trader to break through the cordon, intent on selling trinkets to (or stealing the hides from) we exotic species here in the game park, and we would surely notice it. You have to believe in either a Galactic culture of deadening uniformity, with not a single rebel making trouble, or else a police force of equally terrifying efficiency.

And, even if we are in some form of reserve, how is it we don't see the lights of the towns beyond the fence, the contrails of aircraft in the sky? Even if the aliens are avoiding contact with us, we still ought to see the evidence of rebuilt stars, of the giant energies of starships, beyond our reserve. But we don't.

It may be, of course, that we are surrounded by fake scenery, concealing the truth. Maybe much of what we see *isn't real*.

Solipsism is the philosophical notion that the only absolutely knowable truth is one's own existence. How can I determine if there is any external reality outside my own head? Doctor Johnson rose to this challenge in a blunt way. He kicked a rock and said, 'I refute it thus' . . .

We could surely concede (tentative!) reality to anything we can kick, or touch or taste or smell: anything which reacts with ourselves, as the rock reacted against Johnson's boot. So we can be pretty sure the Earth exists, and humans have kicked rocks as far away as the Moon. We have even handled rocks we believe came from Mars and the asteroid belt (meteorites). And, if our machines can be regarded as extensions of ourselves, our probes have 'kicked' the planets out as far as Neptune.

But maybe we do after all live inside a fake shell of 'fixed stars', as the ancients imagined and as depicted more recently in the movie *The Truman Show*. Maybe the wonderful stellar panoramas we see are *trompe l'oeil* fakes, like the archways to wonderful lands painted on the walls of Renaissance churches; perhaps beyond the walls there is a universe crammed with star cities and wonderful spaceships.

It might be interesting to explore ways of testing this notion. We might look within ourselves, seeking taboos or conditioning that stop us 'seeing' the mechanisms that project the illusion all around us. Or we might try to bounce a radar signal off Pluto or a distant ice moon. If nothing came back from such a 'kick', the plot would thicken indeed . . .

I don't put this paranoid possibility forward seriously – but still, like the Roswell story, it would fit with the facts: it is after all a lot easier to throw a shell around a single world than to camouflage an entire crowded universe.

And if we are trapped inside some giant, fake virtual reality, perhaps it is our duty to crash the program; if we are surrounded by duck blinds we ought to break into them, quacking noisily.

This might seem irresponsible. After all, many of the 'zoo hypothesis' cases outlined above derive from aliens with an altruistic impulse: they are protecting us, if only from ourselves. But even the most benevolent protégé-patron relationship is a relationship of unequals which I, for one, find hard to accept. If they are hiding the truth from me, even if they believe they are caring for me, let them show themselves and justify their actions – to *me*.

The final possible way to resolve Fermi strikes me as even worse than the notion that we are in thrall to secretive superior aliens.

What if, despite our intuition, we are, after all, truly alone? What if our tiny Earth really is the *only* harbour of advanced life and mind in the cosmos?

But if so, how come? As pointed out earlier, it defies our intuition that in such a vast universe life and mind should be restricted to this tiny rock.

Well, it may be that other races have arisen, but all became extinct before meaningful contact was achieved. We can think of a number of ways this could come about. The extinction could be self-inflicted. Rather like the Polynesians, perhaps expansionist species like ourselves must inevitably expire in trashed environments or terrible wars; we may not be able to overcome the dread contradictions of our nature.

Or perhaps our machines will turn on us. Frank Tipler proposed (see Chapter 20) a wave of replicating robots swarming across the Galaxy, turning fallow star systems into bases for making more copies of themselves. If such a probe arrived in an inhabited system – and did not realise it was inhabited – then it could crush the native life without even noticing it was doing so.

Or perhaps the replicating robots are more directly malevolent. Perhaps, through accident or some destructive design, there are killer robots which seek out young worlds like our own in order to destroy them. This has been explored in science fiction by, for example Gregory Benford in his *Galactic Centre* series, and by Fred Saberhagen, whose 'Berserkers' were the relics of interstellar wars.

Again this might seem a paranoid speculation, but it would be consistent with the observed facts. Maybe we don't hear from anybody out there because everybody else is either dead already, or has learned to keep as silent as possible. And all the time we are like baby birds in a nest, noisily cheeping for our parents, while overhead the sky grows black with predators.

Or, of course, the destruction mechanism may be natural. The universe is a violent and dangerous place, not necessarily friendly to such fragile entities as intelligent beings. A supernova explosion could cause devastation to planets like ours over a volume of light years. And astronomers observe far more violent explosions, even than supernovas, all over the sky.

We have learned to recognise gamma ray bursts as the signature of vast explosions in deepest space. (These first came to the notice of US satellites sent into orbit, ironically, to seek the evidence of nuclear explosions on Earth; their records of the far greater cosmic explosions was held back from open inspection for many years.) We are still unsure about the mechanism of a burster; perhaps a particularly massive star explodes, or perhaps exotic objects collide such as neutron stars or even black holes. In a typical burst, there is a pulse of high-energy radiation – gamma rays – followed by cosmic rays, energetic particles, following at a little below lightspeed. These are unimaginably powerful events, emitting more energy in a few seconds than will the sun in all its ten billion years of life.

If such a burst occurred *anywhere within a thousand light years of Earth*, our planet would receive – in a few seconds, mostly in the form of gamma rays – a tenth of its annual energy input from the sun. The ozone layer would be badly damaged; an intense acid rain would follow. The sleeting radiation would disrupt the biosphere, for example by shattering protein molecules.

But the following cosmic rays would be immensely more damaging. Battering into the atmosphere, the rays would create a shower of muons (high-energy subatomic particles), a hard rain from the sky, day after day, subatomic particles each with the punch of a hurled baseball shattering the biomolecules on which life depends. Such is the penetrating power of these muons that even hundreds of metres of water or rock would not be a sufficient shield. Nothing on the surface could survive; only life in the deepest oceans, or buried in the deepest rocks, could ride out the disaster.

This may sound outlandish, but recall the Earth's history is littered by catastrophic extinction events, many of which have yet to be explained.

We can even think of mechanisms for wiping a whole galaxy clean of life: for instance, the collision of one galaxy with another. Our own Galaxy appears to have 'consumed' many smaller star systems in the past, with the resulting release of vast energies. And, even as we speak, our Galaxy is heading for a collision, a few billion years hence, with our largest near galactic neighbour, the great spiral of Andromeda.

But again, we have to remember that consistency is the key. All it would take is *one* species to keep from blowing itself up, and evade the killer robots, and survive the huge extinction events, long enough to expand across the Galaxy, and we would see them, or at least their footprints.

There is a simpler, still more devastating possibility.

Perhaps the evolution of intelligent life is so unlikely that there has been time for it to happen only *once*, here on Earth, in all the universe's long history. Perhaps we find ourselves alone simply because we happen to be the first.

Frank Tipler has argued that humans are the result of ten 'crucial steps' in the evolution of life on Earth:

- the development of DNA
- the invention of oxygen respiration
- the use of glucose in energy metabolism
- the invention of photosynthesis
- the development of mitochondria, energy 'batteries' for complex cells
- the invention of the mechanism of chromosome separation during the reproduction of cells
- the evolution of eyes
- the development of skeletons
- the development of creatures with complex nervous systems
- the evolution of humanity itself.

Perhaps a similar 'ladder' of key steps is essential in the development of any intelligent species, no matter how different in external form from ourselves. And if each of these steps is intrinsically unlikely, then perhaps the evolution of intelligence, the end result of a long series of improbable steps, is itself extremely unlikely.

We should remember that although life on Earth seems to have started as soon as it could after Earth's formation, for billions of years – most of the planet's long history – there was no creature more complex than a single cell anywhere on Earth. And there is much speculation that when the worlds of the Solar System were young, many of them may have been warm and wet, and life sprouted on Earth, Venus, Mars, even Titan, only for it to be rapidly snuffed out by climatic change, everywhere but Earth.

I have to admit that this is the resolution to Fermi I favour. *We must be alone*: the universe is empty save for ourselves, just as it seems at face value; in the face of the objection of universal consistency, no mechanism of misapprehension or extinction or concealment seems credible. But it isn't a resolution I like.

For generations humans have dreamed of finding other minds among the stars: perhaps extremely ancient cultures capable of answering all our questions, and, perhaps, capable of saving us from ourselves. But today, as the sky remains silent, we are beginning to face the possibility that we are in fact alone – the first of all – and, no matter how long and far we look, we will find nobody out there to ease our loneliness.

In which case, perhaps, our duty is to overcome the hostility of the universe to life and mind, to allow those who follow us a better chance. And the first step in achieving that, of course, is not to wipe ourselves out.

For if we allow ourselves to become extinct, the universe may not evolve another species capable of mind in all its long history. The unseen universe will continue to unfold according to the mindless logic of physical law; but hope and love and beauty will die with us, leaving nobody even to mourn our passing.

And if we are alone, then in some senses the ancients were right and Copernicus wrong: the Earth, small and fragile as it may be, really is the most important place in the universe.

Throughout the history of science and philosophy, paradoxes have pointed the way forward to new understanding. Whatever its resolution, the Fermi Paradox is one of the richest unanswered questions today, and its study, one way or the other, will surely have profound implications for us and our destiny.

But it is a strange and remarkable thought that ultimately *it does not matter* if we find the aliens or not. For in the end, all life will face the same challenges, when the stars begin to die.

FIVE

Deep Future

Chapter 23

The Black Hole Miners

The finer part of mankind will, in all likelihood, never
perish – they will migrate from sun to sun as they go
out. And so there is no end to life, to intellect and the
perfection of humanity; its progress is everlasting.

— **Konstantin Tsiolkovskii**

I t is a strange paradox that the further we look into the future, the
more precise our predictions become.

The near future, with all its economic, technological, environmental and human variables, is a complex fog, its outlines difficult to
discern. A little beyond – Fermi notwithstanding – it may be that we
will find ourselves in a greater fog, inhabited by beings whose nature
we can't begin to guess at.

But as we look into the deep future, the winds of time blow
stronger, and the fog begins to clear. We still aren't sure about the
detail of physical law, of course; but we can be confident that
whatever creatures inhabit that long twilight must be increasingly
constrained by the iron logic of the Second Law of Thermodynamics,
which describes the increase of entropy in the universe, a measure of
how much usable energy is left for life to exploit.

Just as the most complex of human lives resolves itself at last in the
simplicity of death, so the story of the universe becomes clarified as
its energy dwindles and possibilities diminish.

Konstantin Tsiolkovskii, quoted at the opening of the chapter, was a great visionary of the human future in space, and his words are still uplifting. And yet he was wrong.

We may indeed migrate from sun to sun; but in the end, *all* the suns will go out. And then we will have to find a new way to live.

You are drifting in space. The sky, at first, seems utterly dark, as if all the stars have died.

Gradually you see something. At first it is only a diffuse red wash. Perhaps there is a slightly brighter central patch, surrounded by a blood-coloured river studded here and there by dim yellow sparkles. You wonder if the shapes you are perceiving are real, or artefacts of your imagination.

Now you see that the great central glow is a pink-white ball, embedded in a diffuse cloud. You think you can see ribbons, streamers in the cloud, as if material is being dragged into that pink maw at the centre. The core and its orbiting cloud seem to be embedded in a ragged disc, a thing of tatters and streamers of gas.

It looks like a galaxy – but it is a caricature of the bright, vibrant star system you inhabit. You can make out no structure in the disc, no trace of spiral arms, no lanes of light and darkness. And that central mound is much more pronounced than our Galaxy's core, as if it is a tumour that has grown, eating this cosmic wreck from the inside.

This *is* a galaxy – indeed, it is our Galaxy – but it is extremely old. Its stars are dying, and there is no material left from which new stars can be formed. Some of the stars have drifted out of the Galaxy. The rest are collapsing into black holes in the disc, radiating gravity energy. That central mass is the giant black hole at the Galaxy's core. In our time it had accreted around a million times the mass of the sun. Even now it is still growing, as star remnants fall into it.

You have travelled deep into the future. The universe is more than a hundred thousand billion years old, some *ten thousand times* its present age, so old that the whole history of our world, from its formation to the twenty-first century, compares to this desert of future time as your very first few hours of existence compare to your whole life.

And as it ages the universe is becoming hostile to life.

Perhaps humans, or other intelligences, still survive by gathering the remnant gases, forming artificial star-birthing clouds: gardening the Galaxy, even so far into the future. But this is fending off the inevitable. When the last stars die, so must life . . .

But must it?

The sun's energy drives the cycles of life on Earth.

At present we get almost all our energy from the sun: either directly from sunlight with solar cells, or indirectly through the solar energy stored by long-dead life as fossil fuels. Visionary engineers (such as Freeman Dyson) have dreams of enclosing our sun in a solid sphere, to capture *all* its energy.

But, like all stars, our sun will die. No more free lunches.

Of course there will be other stars, and perhaps our medium-term destiny is as Tsiolkovskii sketched it: to become interstellar nomads, migrating from star to star.

And new stars will continue to be born for a long time to come. Our Galaxy, in fact, resembles a vast machine for moulding stars out of its interstellar medium. Looking at the Galaxy today, it might seem impossible that such an immense system could one day die. And yet, as the interstellar medium becomes exhausted, die it must.

Sooner or later there will be no more new stars: the existing population of stars is all there will ever be, and they will grow steadily older. And after a hundred thousand billion years, the last of the stars, smallest, longest-lived dwarfs, will reach the end of their lives.

After the last lights go out the universe will become very dark and cold, containing little but cooling dwarf stars and neutron stars and black holes and brown dwarfs, planet-stars like Jupiter too small to burn.

It is still possible for life to draw energy from the star ruins. We can imagine colonies surrounding the cooling corpses of the stars in thin artificial shells. Perhaps we might even collide the brown dwarfs to make their unspent hydrogen fuel burn.

But the energy supply is so thin that life of the vigour and variety we understand it today will be impossible; human life may have to be satisfied with a virtual-reality existence, with consciousness sustained within huge, star-girdling computers. Perhaps the virtual simulations will depict our day, the bright blue morning of the universe.

And this long twilight is going to last many billions of billions of *billions* of years – unimaginable deserts of time – compared to which our era, the era of star formation, will seem as brief as a flashbulb pop. We live in abnormal times, and if we are to survive in the long term we must prepare to inhabit the twilight that is the natural state of the universe.

Fortunately, there is another energy source to dwarf even that of the vanished stars. This is the energy stored in black holes.

Black holes are extremely dense. A hole with the mass of our sun would have a diameter of a few kilometres (compared to the sun's actual size of more than a million kilometres). A black hole, in fact, is so dense that nothing – not even light – can escape its gravitational field. A traveller unlucky enough to fall within a black hole's event horizon would be utterly unable to escape. Bombarded by radiation, ripped apart by tidal forces, she would at last plunge into the 'singularity', a central region of infinite density and zero volume.

Even in our present-day Galaxy black holes can be found. They linger in the disc, relics of collapsed giant stars – and there is that voracious monster in the core, already immense, and growing. It is believed that the extraordinarily powerful objects known as 'quasars' are powered by Galaxy-core black holes.

We think of black holes as destructive and dangerous, gateways to hell. But in the longest of timescales, black holes are life's future.

Suppose you could travel deeper into time, far beyond the wreck of the Galaxy.

This time you are greeted by a point of yellow-white light, sun-like, and you wonder if somehow your long journey through time has looped back on itself, returning you to the dawn of the universe.

But this is no star. The object has structure. A central glaring point is surrounded by a tilted disc, glowing red, within which you can trace a tight spiral pattern. And there seem to be lines of light tracing out from the poles of that central gleam, needle-thin.

Further out you see discs and knots of dull red matter, much smaller than the big bright central object. The central light actually casts shadows through the crowded space around it, shadows that must be thousands of light years long.

This is a new metamorphosis of the ageing Galaxy, but this assemblage is much smaller than the Galaxy of your day. Ninety per cent of the star remnants in the Galaxy have evaporated away by chance collisions and gravitational slingshots, and the rest are gathering in the giant black hole at the core. The light you see is coming from the central accretion disc, where matter is falling into the core black hole. The hole itself is probably a few light-months across. The beams coming from the poles are plasma directed by the magnetic field of the hole.

It is intensely bright, more energetic than the combined fusion energy of all the Galaxy's stars in their heyday.

It is all oddly beautiful, a sculpture of light and blood-red smoke. But it is chilling, inhuman; there is nothing you can recognise here, nothing that looks like a star.

Nevertheless there is life here, you slowly realise: hints of structure, immense almost beyond imagination, in the shattered clouds that orbit that central black hole.

You have travelled a trillion trillion years. The universe is ten *billion* times as old as the age of dying stars and brown dwarf farmers. And in this remote age, the black hole miners are at work.

How would we extract usable energy from such unpromising, hostile objects as black holes? We can think of a number of ways, all of which boil down to extracting gravitational energy from the black holes.

Black holes are not in fact perfectly 'black'. Because of quantum effects they give off a slow trickle of radiation, called 'Hawking radiation'. This is thin gruel, but would provide a usable amount of energy from a large enough hole.

Another approach is based on the fact that as black holes consume ordinary matter, they compress it so much that energy is released. So, if you lived in a community orbiting a black hole, you could simply throw your garbage into the hole and feed off the resulting radiation as the waste is crushed to fusion densities.

Another technique is merging holes. If you coalesce two black holes, you get a single, larger hole – with an event horizon ringing like a bell – but you also get a monumental release of gravitational energy in the form of *gravity waves*.

Perhaps the most promising mining technology candidate is the Penrose process. A fifth of a spinning hole's energy is stored in a vast tornado-like swirl of space and time, dragged around by the hole's immense inertia. You could tap this energy by enclosing the hole in a great mesh of superconducting cables, threading the tornado swirl with a magnetic field, to form a giant electrical power generator.

The age of the black hole miners is remote. By then the universe will have expanded to some ten thousand *trillion* times its size in our day. To the miners the whole evolution of *our* universe, from Big Bang to present day, will seem as brief, as insignificant, as the first few *hours* after the Big Bang is to us.

But perhaps they will remember us, as we remember the simpler creatures from whom we evolved.

The black holes are the greatest energy sources in the universe, sources so great they outshine our fusion-driven stars as if they were candles. It may be that *this* era is to be the peak of intelligent life.

But even the black hole gravity mines will at last be exhausted.

Even without their tapping by intelligence, all the black holes in the universe are slowly evaporating: Hawking radiation amounts to a slow leak of energy. And the smaller the hole, the faster it decays.

It is believed that very small black holes were created in the ferocious pressures of the Big Bang – perhaps with the mass of a mountain, about the size of an atomic nucleus. Such holes must already have evaporated (thought slightly larger holes might still survive).

In the future, larger and larger holes must begin to evaporate. In their last seconds the holes become energetic, exploding like a nuclear weapon: the universe will still produce occasional fireworks, even far in the future.

The evaporation of a black hole even the mass of the sun will take a *long* time. But ultimately even the largest natural black hole – with the mass of a supercluster of galaxies, some trillions of stars – is going to evaporate away. And what then?

Let us step further ahead.

We are considering very deep futures now: *ten thousand times* further even than the early days of the black hole miners' empire, when medium-sized black holes could still exist. *Those* days, long after the death of the stars, which seem so remote from us, now seem like the springtime of the universe.

As for our world, it is but a detail of the Big Bang, lost in the afterglow of Creation.

And yet there is structure, and life. You make out the faintest of patterns: charcoal grey on black, almost beyond your ability to resolve, a pattern of neat regular triangles, a structure that spans space.

It is a giant geodesic dome – or rather a net, hundreds of thousands of light years wide. And there's only one thing worth collecting, this far into the future.

Through the interstices of the dome you see a complex, textured curtain of grey-pink light. The curtain is made up of black hole event horizons: giant holes, galactic supercluster mass and above, gathered in and brought to this place. They are orbiting each other, their event horizons distorting. On cosmic scales the motion is very rapid, unimaginably violent – though frozen to stillness by our mayfly human perception.

The holes, gathered from across the universe, are being merged in a hierarchy of more and more massive holes, in order to stretch out their lifetimes. The geodesic sphere is an energy collector, designed to tap the last energy sources: the slow Hawking radiation of the black holes. Anything still alive must be living on those struts, feeding off the last trickle of free energy.

Our descendants, walled in by physical law, have had to learn to manage their black hole resources.

The supercluster-scale holes are the largest to have formed in nature, with masses of maybe a hundred trillion suns – but even they will evaporate away. But you can stretch out the lifetimes of black holes. If you combine two holes, you get a more massive hole – which will be cooler, and so it will evaporate more slowly. (We don't know, incidentally, how to move a black hole. Maybe we could use Hawking radiation as a rocket. Luckily, there is plenty of time to figure out this detail.)

Our descendants will coalesce holes in hierarchies all over the reachable universe. The engineering details are tricky. You have to bring the holes together fast enough that they don't evaporate away before you've harvested them. On the other hand it mustn't be so rapid that you form a hole so huge it evaporates too slowly and you are starved of usable energy.

And as larger and larger holes are gathered, so a larger fraction of the universe must be reached. It will be a mighty universe-spanning project.

But the energy flow will be vanishingly small. Maybe our descendants will eke out their dilute resources by submitting to long hibernations, stretching an hour of awareness across a million years. Or perhaps they will be conscious in this ruin of a universe: frozen into their black hole cage, unable to move, trapped like Judas in the lowest circle of Hell.

Thus, by moving masses the size of clusters of galaxies, life will survive trillions upon trillions of years – but not for ever. For there is a catch.

You have to build some kind of framework around the black holes, a structure to gather the energy. The structure must grow with time, as you collect more holes. And even if matter itself doesn't decay over such immense periods (it may), the structure has to be upgraded, repaired. The maintenance requirements go *up* with time, because the structure is getting bigger, but the energy available is going *down* . . . It's a squeeze. And it isn't possible to win.

This black hole harvesting will be magnificent and it will last an unimaginable time, far beyond puny human scales. But for all its magnificence, this frozen empire is doomed.

What then? What is the ultimate fate of the universe – and of life?

Chapter 24

A Universe in Ruins

All the labours of the ages, all the devotion, all the inspiration, all the noonday brightness of the human genius, are destined to end in the vast death of the Solar System, and . . . the whole temple of Man's achievement must inevitably be buried beneath the debris of a universe in ruins . . .

— Bertrand Russell

A knowledge of one's own mortality is an unwelcome part of growing up. Of course we can comfort ourselves with the thought that what we leave behind will live on: children, monuments of stone, business empires – or books. But maybe there is a defining moment in the maturing of a species when it realises that it too faces ultimate extinction, that all its works will amount to nought.

Is there a way out? If the universe is to end – well, how, exactly? And is there anything we can do about it?

The science of eschatology, the study of the end of things, was born in the nineteenth century with the notion of entropy, inflicted on us by Rudolf Clausius. The dread Second Law of Thermodynamics dictates that global entropy must increase to a maximum, and the far future of mankind, increasingly starved of energy by this 'Heat Death', looked bleak indeed, in a universe with a pretty profound design flaw.

The first serious modern attempt to look for a loophole in that pesky Second Law was made by the Princeton physicist Freeman Dyson, who in 1979 delivered a landmark series of lectures based on hard thinking about what the far future might actually be like. Dyson sketched, complete with numerical estimates, the farthest future of an open universe (that is, a universe which continues to expand) and the types of physical processes which might prevail.

The endless expansion of an open universe is not the only possibility, however. Perhaps we live in a *closed* universe: that is, we may face a future in which the universe eventually ceases its expansion and collapses back to a 'Big Crunch', a time-reversed rerun of the Big Bang.

At first glance the prospect of being Crunched out of existence seems even more unbearable than 'Heat Death': Freeman Dyson remarked that the closed universe gave him 'a feeling of claustrophobia, to imagine our whole universe confined within a box'. How could we survive such a devastating terminus?

In 1994 physicist Frank Tipler gave eschatological optimists a great fillip. Tipler showed, at least to his own satisfaction, that it would be possible for far-future intelligences to manipulate the final Crunch in a collapsing universe (essentially by causing the universe to oscillate wildly) to provide an energy source that would, at the Omega Point, the final Eschaton, become *infinite*.

And with this infinite energy, it would be possible to think an infinite number of thoughts, to have an infinite number of experiences – and so to achieve eternal life, even in the finite time left.

But Tipler, the biggest of thinkers, did not stop there. The giant computing machines at the Omega Point might be able to recreate in an exactly detailed simulation *every* sentient being in the universe's long history (in fact, they would be *bound* to do this, said Tipler). And by invoking philosophical principles about identity, Tipler was able to claim that this giant holodeck heaven would amount to a literal resurrection of all of us, of you, at the end of time. Not of a copy of you, but *you*. Tipler identified many elements of this vision with theologies, particularly the Christian – and succeeded in enthralling and offending almost everybody.

It is an understatement to say that not all physicists agree with Tipler's conclusions. For one thing Tipler seems to have confused the properties of the final limit of his universal manipulation with the process of that manipulation. The physicist David Deutsch has speculated how it would actually be to approach Tipler's Omega Point: to struggle without end to maintain a haven for life and mind within the crashing walls of the cosmos, knowing that a single lapse of concentration will result in universal doom.

And Tipler's theory is simplistic. His 'heaven' is a place where we will be literally resurrected, but in an optimised existence – so that we will each, for example, meet the perfect sexual partner. This kind of sugar-coated thinking was surpassed in sophistication not only by thinkers of centuries past but also by my teachers in my own long-gone childhood Catholic education.

Still, flawed or not, Tipler's synthesis does provide a way past the end of things. And its appeal is strong. The proposition overlaps with the Christian view of the universe as an orderly place: a linear story proceeding from a beginning to an end, a story which will be, in this view, under our control. And, remarkably, it offers the chance of species survival *and* individual immortality.

But Tipler's future is probably a glittering illusion. At the time of writing, the best evidence from the astronomers is that the universe is not destined for a Big Crunch after all, but for an endless expansion – and, in fact, that expansion is accelerating.

Still, Dyson and Tipler can't both be right. It is a strange thought that in the very far future one of these men may be utterly forgotten and the other may be remembered as the most remarkable prophet in history.

Let us look ahead, then, using Dyson as our best-guess guide to the deepest of futures, the very last days.

On the longest of timescales, nothing can survive. No human work can persist, no matter how well constructed, how well preserved – no city, no monument, no tomb, no work of art – for *matter itself* is probably unstable.

The protons and neutrons contained in the nuclei of atoms decay to simpler forms. It's slow. We know that the decay must take at least a billion *billion* years. (You can tell it's at least this long because you are alive: your body contains so many protons and neutrons that any faster decay rate would produce enough energetic particles to kill you by cancer.) But given a long enough time, the decay is inevitable.

Even black holes evaporate, as we have seen. The last holes will produce photons and neutrinos, and some heavy particles, but they will decay away too. What then?

Let us make one more journey into the future.

Start with a second.

Zoom out. Factor it up to get the life of the Earth, with that second a glowing moment embedded within. Zoom out *again*, to get a new period so long Earth's lifetime is reduced, to scale, to the span of that original second. Then zoom out again. And again and again and *again* . . .

It is dark here.

There are no dead stars, no rogue planets. The last solid matter has long evaporated, burned up by proton decay, leaving nothing but a thin smoke of neutrinos drifting out at lightspeed.

But still there is life, movement. Vast, wispy entities cruised across space-time's swelling breast.

For ages the black hole engineers struggled to maintain their huge geodesic nets, to gather more material to replace what decayed away. It was magnificent, futile. The last structures failed, the last black holes allowed to evaporate. The conflux of minds dispersed, flowing out over the expanding universe like water running into sand.

Even now, of course, there is *something* rather than nothing. Around you is an unimaginably thin plasma: free electrons and positrons, decayed from the last of the Big Bang's hydrogen, orbiting in giant, slow circles, atoms light years across.

This cold soup is the last refuge of humanity.

Freeman Dyson's philosophy was essentially optimistic; he sought to demonstrate that as far ahead as it was possible to look the universe would continue to evolve. The dead hand of the Second

Law will hold overall sway, as available energy sources diminish. But Dyson showed that it ought to be possible, in principle at least, for an intelligence to extract an *infinite* amount of experience – counted as changes in state, 'thoughts' – from a *finite* amount of energy, perhaps by enduring long periods of dreamless hibernation.

The people of this age drift past you like clouds, immense, slow, coded in enormous wispy atoms. Free energy is dwindling to zero, time stretching to infinity. It takes these cloud-beings longer to complete a single thought than it once took species to rise and fall on Earth.

It doesn't matter. They have plenty of time. Time, in fact, is all they have left.

And even now, you suspect, they cling to the solace of community; and you feel a flicker of kinship with them, with your own remote grandchildren.

This book has focused on an expansive future for mankind.

We have explored our species' first tentative attempts to determine how we might be able to survive into the deep future, for an indefinitely long time; how we may outlive the death of the Earth, the death of the sun and other stars, even the end of matter itself. We have crossed billions of billions of billions of years – and we have barely glimpsed the possibilities for mankind, for our descendants.

But we have no preordained right to survive.

Chapter 25

After Man

There is no way back into the past. The choice is the
Universe – or nothing.

— H. G. Wells

L ook around. You are at the centre of a once-great city. But there is
no artificial light, no traffic noise, no people.

It is the year 2010. The last human disappeared a year ago.

The first stages of the destruction of the cities are familiar to every
urbanite battling to keep the weeds from her patio or drive. After a
year, weeds like dandelions are growing in the gutters and the frost-
cracked concrete. Some imported shrubs like buddleia are more
aggressive, with roots powerful enough to penetrate bricks and
mortar. The debris from these first plants forms a soil over the
concrete, allowing the spread of other plants. Grasses, shrubs and
trees take root in the deepening soil; tree roots smash through what is
left of the pavement.

We can see this process in action today. The modern city of Pripyat
was built to house nuclear workers from Chernobyl. After a decade of
abandonment its open spaces were green, its paving stones so
smashed and lifted by tree roots they looked as if they had been
through an earthquake.

After five to ten years, storm-sparked fire is likely in the leaf-strewn cities. The burned material provides nitrogen to speed the growth of the plants.

Any gutted buildings surviving the fires may be pounded by another great natural force: floods. The embankments and barriers protecting London from the Thames, for example, would soon yield to erosion and subsidence, and land along the river bank would revert to marsh.

As the plants recolonise the cities, butterflies, bees and other insects follow; then, as the food chain builds up, the birds, and at last mammals.

Not all animals fare well. Animals like pigeons and rats which depend on humans for food disappear, in favour of field mice and other countryside species. Descendants of larger dogs survive in the wild; and cats descended from pets once fondly spoiled by old ladies have little trouble recontacting their wilder instincts.

But the balance of nature is not as it was before man. Many non-native species of animals and plants, imported for gardens, parks and zoos – maples and conifers, parakeets, feral pigs, deer – survive here, living clues to any alien archaeologists that intelligence was once at work here, disturbing the primaeval order.

Amidst the spreading greenery, the surviving buildings are battered by weather and erosion. Without repainting and main-tenance, bridge spans do not last more than fifty years. Our modern steel and concrete buildings, like city-centre office blocks, fare better: ivy dangles from the skyscrapers that still protrude, for a time, from the green layers of forest. In fact, the air and rain is clean of the acidic pollutants that damage our buildings in the present day. But they have lost their window glass, and are scorched by fire.

Wooden structures are the first to vanish completely, their fabric destroyed by the patient attention of insects.

Stone buildings last longer, at least those far from the unstable land close to the rivers, but as more trees take root among the rubble, more walls are brought down. The very mortar of Hadrian's Wall (built c. AD 122, almost two thousand years old) has long crumbled to dust, and frost and lichen are destroying the stones themselves.

After five centuries, the stone buildings are reduced to hummocks under the turf.

The skyscrapers survive a little longer, as long as their foundations hold against the rise of the water tables. But corroding concrete at last exposes the steel bars that reinforce the buildings. After that, the collapse is swift.

It seems unlikely that any modern building would last as long as the great stone constructions of the Middle Ages. The oldest castle in the UK, at Chepstow, Monmouthshire, dates from AD 1067. Many buildings and structures have survived longer still: the oldest Egyptian pyramid is the Djoser at Saqqara, dating back to c.2630 BC, and the earliest part of Stonehenge dates from c.2950 BC. Modern buildings in a city like London, built on a flood plain, rest on much less stable foundations, subject to inundation and natural earth movements.

The destruction of the buildings, subject to weathering and the action of life, and without anybody to maintain them, is steady and inexorable. Not even the most robust of our structures will survive more than a few tens of millennia.

Fossil human skeletons will surely turn up here and there. We are very numerous and, with our habit of burying our dead, we are giving our remains a head start in preservation.

It is unlikely that any soft parts would survive more than a few tens of millennia, however. Today we occasionally find exceptionally preserved humans – bog bodies, ice men, mummies – their remains protected, by accident or design, by freezing, pickling or drying. In 1900 the head of a Siberian mammoth was thawed after being frozen for forty thousand years; the meat was well enough preserved that wolves were prepared to eat it. But such preservation can only work as long as environmental conditions, such as temperature and humidity, stay constant. Over a million years or more, this is unlikely.

Still, soft body parts can leave traces. Skin impressions from dinosaur 'mummies', a *hundred* million years old, have occasionally been found, in places where the skin lasted long enough to leave a mark in the enclosing, hardening rock. Bodies trapped in rocks formed in volcanic eruptions, like the hollows left by the burial of the inhabitants of Pompeii, can leave similar 'negative' impressions.

It is strange to think that the best clue to the shape of our bodies in the remote future might be the impression left by a 1920s gangster in his 'concrete overcoat'.

Our abandoned artefacts, buried with our bones in the gathering layers of sediment, may fare better.

The oldest weapon discovered dates from c.200,000 BC: a wooden spear found near Clacton in Essex in 1911. The oldest tools may be two and a half *million* years old, a collection of chipped pebbles and scratched bones found with the remains of an early hominid called *Australopithecus*. Compared to that, even deep-buried nuclear waste is short-lived; plutonium has a half-life of twenty-four thousand years, so that only a few per cent remains after just a hundred thousand years. It may be that the simple tools of chipped stone left by our ancestors may last longer than any remnants of our more sophisticated age.

But not just bones, tools and body parts leave traces for the future. We have observed dinosaur nests, burrows and even footprints. As a species we have worked much harder at disturbing the Earth than the dinosaurs ever did.

Our 'footprints' will include roads, foundations, hard-wearing artificial rocks like concrete and brick, iron, copper, steel and plastic: a thick layer left by centuries of building, shot through with pipes, tunnels, cables and pilings reaching deep underground. Even after the buildings are gone, such a stratum can survive indefinitely if it is buried sufficiently quickly, and escapes erosion.

On the surface of Earth, erosion is savage and unrelenting and, on geological timescales, surprisingly rapid. Wind carries away particles from rocks and soils; rivers carry sediments to the sea; waves grind up pebbles and eat away at cliffs. Earth's dynamic geology keeps its surface young, compared to static, smaller worlds like the Moon and Mars, but it is a process which leads to the inexorable destruction of traces of human presence.

Earth keep its surface young.

As the continents work through their stately dance, some parts of the Earth's surface are rising, and some are falling. Surprisingly, perhaps, it is the parts that are *falling* that will be best at preserving traces of mankind, for they allow remains to be buried before being eroded. In regions of uplift, even the foundations of the greatest cities will crumble and wash away to the welcoming sea. This will probably be the fate of the cities of West Coast America, Japan, and stable Australia. But European cities like Amsterdam and Barcelona, and cities in India, central Asia and the African rift valley will probably leave long-lasting traces.

Sea level change is also crucial, however. A rapid rise in sea level – caused for instance by the disintegration of the West Antarctic Ice Sheet – while catastrophic for mankind, would serve to drown and therefore preserve many coastal cities.

Our surviving remains will be crushed by an increasing weight of sediment above them. But this need not destroy their identity; fossil shells, long buried, are still recognisable as shells.

Concrete may be destroyed, or at least altered, by chemical changes. But the humble brick will probably survive. A brick is just a lump of clay shock-heated so its minerals change and fuse: mudstone, mud baked by lava, is a natural analogue, and can survive for billions of years, if buried. Glass is unstable over millions of years, becoming opaque as tiny crystals form, but glass fragments retain their shape. Milky-white bottles that once contained beer or soda might persist for millions of years in the strata of the future.

It may be, however, that the most identifiable signature of our presence will not be an artefact at all, but a chemical remnant of our pollution. We have spread concentrations of a host of metals like lead, mercury, cadmium and copper across land and sea, an exotic stratum that will survive deep into time.

Artefacts away from Earth, such as probes in deep space, will survive longer.

But all such objects in the inner Solar System are subject to a constant sandblasting from micrometeorites, and will eventually erode to dust.

On the patient Moon, the last traces of Apollo – footprints, flags, plaques and all – will surely be gone after ten million years.

On longer timescales, of course, Earth itself is doomed. In five billion years the sun will start burning helium instead of hydrogen, and expand to a red giant. Earth itself may be engulfed – rocks, tectonic plates, artefacts and all – and any last trace of ourselves will finally be destroyed.

Our most enduring monuments of all will be the four interstellar spacecraft we have launched: the Voyagers and Pioneers, launched to the outer planets in the 1970s by NASA, and now escaping from the Solar System altogether.

Right now Voyager One is flying high above the plane of the ecliptic, that invisible sheet in space which contains the orbits of the major planets. Voyager weighs around a tonne, and is about as big as a small house. Racing across space at more than a million kilometres per day, Voyager One is heading for the stars.

It takes twenty thousand years for Voyager to cross the Oort Cloud, the sun's immense swarm of comets. Then, its power and radio transmitter long dead, Voyager embarks on an endless circling of the heart of the Milky Way Galaxy.

In the silent calm of interstellar space there is almost nothing to damage the derelict craft. The stars are so sparsely scattered that Voyager never encounters another stellar system. But at last the slow sublimation of metal causes Voyager's aluminium structure to collapse. The fragments of the spacecraft – instrument booms and power generator, pitted and tarnished, metal walls reduced to a paper thickness – drift away from each other, so that the ruin of the spacecraft is surrounded by a cloud of glittering metal dust.

Thus Voyager dies: billions of years after the first clumsily chopped stone axe, twenty thousand light years from the sun, the last human artefact in existence.

A possible future. But not the only future.

The choice is ours.

Further Reading

Part One: A Dangerous Century

David Brin, *The Transparent Society* (Addison Wesley, 1998).

Richard Leakey and Roger Lewin, *The Sixth Extinction: Biodiversity and Its Survival* (Weidenfeld & Nicolson, 1996).

John Leslie, *The End of the World* (Routledge, 1996).

Charles Sheffield, *Borderlands of Science* (Baen, 1999).

Part Two: Into That Silent Sea

Stephen Baxter, 'How NASA Lost the Case for Mars in 1969', *Spaceflight* vol. 38, p. 191, June 1996.

Andrew Chaikin, *Man on the Moon* (Michael Joseph, 1994).

R. D. Launius, *NASA: A History of the US Civil Space Programme* (Krieger Publishing Co., 1994).

Walter A. McDougall, *The Heavens and the Earth* (Basic Books, 1985).

Melvyn Smith, *An Illustrated History of Space Shuttle* (Foulis, 1985).

Part Three: Sister Worlds

Stephen Baxter, 'The Hidden Ocean: Mining Deep Water on the

Moon', *Journal of the British Interplanetary Society* vol. 51, pp. 75–80, 1998.

Peter Cattermole, *Mars* (Chapman & Hall, 1992).

Martyn Fogg, *Terraforming: Engineering Planetary Environments* (Society of Automotive Engineers, 1995).

John S. Lewis, *Mining the Sky* (Addison Wesley, 1996).

Jonathan Lunine, 'Does Titan Have Oceans?', *American Scientist* vol. 82, 1994, pp. 134–144.

Mikhail Marov and David Grinspoon, *The Planet Venus* (Yale University Press, 1998).

W. W. Mendell, ed., *Lunar Bases and Space Activities of the 21st Century* (Lunar and Planetary Institute, 1985).

Gerard K. O'Neill, *The High Frontier: Human Colonies in Space* (William Morrow, 1977).

Carl Sagan, *Pale Blue Dot* (Headline, 1995).

P. Spudis, *The Once and Future Moon* (Smithsonian Press, 1996).

D. Wilhelms, *To a Rocky Moon: A Geologist's History of Lunar Exploration* (University of Arizona Press, 1993).

Robert Zubrin, *The Case for Mars* (Free Press, 1996).

Part Four: Pilots of the Purple Twilight

John Barrow and Frank Tipler, *The Anthropic Cosmological Principle* (Oxford, 1986).

Adrian Berry, *The Giant Leap: Mankind Heads for the Stars* (Headline, 1999).

David Brin, 'The Great Silence', *Quarterly Journal of the Royal Astronomical Society* vol. 24, pp. 283–309, 1983.

Paul Davies, *Are We Alone?* (Penguin, 1995).

N. Henbest and H. Couper, *The Guide to the Galaxy* (Cambridge, 1994).

E. Mallove and G. Matloff, *The Starflight Handbook* (Wiley, 1989).

Marshall T. Savage, *The Millennial Project: Colonising the Galaxy in Eight Easy Steps* (Little, Brown, 1994).

Kip Thorne, *Black Holes and Time Warps* (W. W. Norton, 1994).

Part Five: Deep Future

Fred Adams and Greg Laughlin, *The Five Ages of the Universe* (Free Press, 1999).

David Deutsch, *The Fabric of Reality* (Penguin, 1997).

Freeman Dyson, 'Time Without End: Physics and Biology in an Open Universe', *Review of Modern Physics* vol. 51, pp. 447–60, 1979.

Steven Frautschi, 'Entropy in an Expanding Universe', *Science* vol. 217, pp. 593–599, 1982.

Frank Tipler, *The Physics of Immortality* (Doubleday, 1994).